MW00637852

ENCYCLOPEDIA OF *Science*

Blackline Masters

LEARNING RESOURCES®

VERNON HILLS • KING'S LYNN

INTRODUCTION

The *Encyclopedia of Science Blackline Masters* is a convenient, ready-to-use compilation of graphic organizing tools specifically aligned with the National Science Education Standards (NSES). Each page is arranged for easy reproduction as worksheets or overhead transparencies. Tabs are used to categorize these visual tools into five sections for quick location. The graphic organizers within each tab include:

- Semantic Maps for Concept and Vocabulary Understanding
- Properties for Observation, Classification, Comparing and Contrasting
- Cause and Effect and Extending the Senses
- Scientific Method for Research and Experimentation
- Graphs and Measurement for Data Collection and Analysis

Unlike other tools, graphic organizers are flexible and can be utilized for more than one purpose. Graphic organizers can visually show the order and completeness of thought processes, connections, and meaning making. Teachers can easily incorporate these blackline masters into instructional activities to help students generate visual maps throughout discussions, labs, and during the reading, writing and research processes. Other uses facilitate student development in observations, property identification, comparison and contrast, cause and effect, sequence, and analysis. Graphic organizers make great assessment tools to check for student understanding and to quickly identify misunderstandings. The versatility of the *Encyclopedia of Science Blackline Masters* offers endless possibilities for instruction, activities and projects.

Research-based practice relies on graphic organizers as powerful tools to help students organize and extend their thinking throughout the learning process. Capturing your students' thinking process and providing them with visual tools to facilitate student understanding is what the *Encyclopedia of Science Blackline Masters* is all about.

TABLE OF CONTENTS

Semantic Maps
Concepts

E-Chart . . . 1
Hierarchy Tier . . . 2
Spider Map . . . 3
Concept Chart . . . 4
Characteristic Web . . . 5
Analogy Comparison . . . 6
Concept Map 1 . . . 7
Concept Map 2 . . . 8
Tree Diagram . . . 9
Leaf Web . . . 10
Sun Web . . . 11
Bulls-eye Organizer . . . 12
Concept Wheel 1 . . . 13
Concept Wheel 2 . . . 14
Concept w/Examples . . . 15
Cluster Web 1 . . . 16
Cluster Web 2 . . . 17
Cluster Web 3 . . . 18
Concept Map–Six Characteristics . . . 19
Diagram A–Two Characteristics . . . 20
Diagram B–Two Characteristics . . . 21
Diagram C–Three Characteristics . . . 22
Main Idea Map . . . 23
Cluster Web 4 . . . 24
Cluster Web 5 . . . 25
Cluster Web 6 . . . 26
Cluster Web 7 . . . 27
Cluster Web 8 . . . 28
ABC Brainstorm . . . 29
4 x 5 Blank Grid . . . 30

Vocabulary

Frayer Model A . . . 31
Frayer Model B . . . 32
Vocabulary Chart . . . 33
Word Association . . . 34
Word Analogy . . . 35
Word Map . . . 36
Word Chart: Context and Connection . . . 37
Word Chart: Examples and Characteristics . . . 38
Word Chart: Comparisons . . . 39
T-Chart . . . 40

Properties
Observations

T-Diagram . . . 41
Balance Scale . . . 42

AB Comparison 43
Illustrate and Describe 44
Properties 45
Illustrate Circles 46
Illustrate Squares 47
Illustrate – Six Squares A 48
Illustrate – Six Squares B 49
2 x 3 Grid 50
Attributes 1 51
Attributes 2 52

Classification

General to Specific 53
Hierarchy Map 54
Jellyfish Map 55
Column Diagram 56
Pyramid Diagram 57
Funnel Diagram 58
Ascending Order 59
Wedding Cake: Six Levels 60
Cumulative Map 61
Staircase Diagram 62
Attribute Map 1 63
Attribute Map 2 64
Classification Chart 65
Punnett Squares 66
Classification Cluster 67
Category Chart 1 68
Category Chart 2 69
Category Chart 3 70
Category Chart 4 71
Property Matrix 1 72
Property Matrix 2 73
Property Matrix 3 74
Property Matrix 4 75
Deduction Chart 76
Category and Family Web 77

Compare and Contrast

Alike/Different Rectangles 78
Alike/Different Chart 79
H Diagram 80
X Diagram 81
Y Diagram 82
Venn Diagram 83
Venn Diagram: Three Comparisons 84
Venn Diagram ABC 85
Triangle Diagram 86
Rectangle Diagram 87
Comparison Map 1 88
Comparison Map 2 89
Comparison Map 3 90

Comparison Map 4 . . . 91
Comparison: Three Objects A. . . . 92
Comparison: Three Objects B . . . 93
Tic-Tac-Toe Chart . . . 94

Patterns and Cycles

Primary Cycle of Events (3) . . . 95
Primary Cycle of Events (4) . . . 96
Primary Cycle of Events (5) . . . 97
Cycle of Events (4) . . . 98
Cycle of Events (6) . . . 99
Cycle Circle (3) . . . 100
Cycle Circle (4) . . . 101
Cycle Circle (5) . . . 102
Cycle Description Wheel . . . 103
Event Pattern . . . 104

Sequence of Events

Lenses (4). . . . 105
Four Event Sequence. . . . 106
Season Box . . . 107
Season Circle . . . 108
Circle Sequence . . . 109
Four Column Chart. . . . 110
Step-by-Step Chart. . . . 111
Event Ladder . . . 112
Event Sketch . . . 113
Episodic Six Events . . . 114
Episodic Nine Events . . . 115
Sequence Comparison . . . 116
Sequence of Ten. . . . 117
Event Matrix . . . 118
Timeline 1 . . . 119
Timeline 2 . . . 120
Chain of Events 1 . . . 121
Chain of Events 2 . . . 122
Chain of Events 3 . . . 123
Chain of Events 4 . . . 124
Flow Chart 1 . . . 125
Flow Chart 2 . . . 126
Event Lattice. . . . 127
T-Chart . . . 128

Cause and Effect

Primary Cause and Effect. . . . 129
Cause and Effect – Squares. . . . 130
Cause and Two Effects. . . . 131
Cause and Three Effects . . . 132
4 Causes/2 Effects . . . 133
Fishbone: 4 Causes and Effect(s) . . . 134
Fishbone: 6 Causes and Effect(s) . . . 135
Cause/Effect Chain 1 . . . 136

Cause/Effect Chain 2 . . . 137
Cause and Effect Diagram . . . 138
Cause and Effect Relationship . . . 139
Arrow By-Product . . . 140
Physical/Chemical Change . . . 141
Reaction Chart . . . 142
Reaction Diagram . . . 143
Speculation About Effects . . . 144
Cause/Effect Prediction . . . 145
Counter-Factuals . . . 146

Extending the Senses

Four Square . . . 147
Sketch and Describe 1 . . . 148
Sketch and Describe 2 . . . 149
Sensory Observations 1 . . . 150
Sensory Observations 2 . . . 151

Research

KWL Chart . . . 152
KWS Chart . . . 153
DRTA Chart . . . 154
Five W's Star . . . 155
Five W's + H . . . 156
Question Generator . . . 157
Research Questions . . . 158
Research Organizer . . . 159
Question Notes 1 . . . 160
Question Notes 2 . . . 161
Question Notes 3 . . . 162
Question Notes 4 . . . 163
Book Resource . . . 164
Magazine Resource . . . 165
Encyclopedia Resource . . . 166
Internet Resource . . . 167
Internet Search . . . 168
QuIP Map: Three Sources . . . 169
QuIP Map: Four Sources . . . 170
Paraphrase Map . . . 171
Writing Organizer . . . 172
Summary-Response . . . 173

Experimentation

Question/Prediction Chart . . . 174
Predict/Explain/Find Out . . . 175
Prediction Map . . . 176
Experiment Chart . . . 177
Experiment Map . . . 178
Demonstration Map . . . 179
Discrepant Event 1 . . . 180
Discrepant Event 2 . . . 181
Invention Map 1 . . . 182

Invention Map 2 183
Summary List 184
3-2-1 185
Knowledge Chart 186
Synthesis Journal 187
Learning Log. 188

Graphs and Measurement

XY Graph 189
XY Graph (3) 190
Interval Scale 191
Interval Scale (2) 192
Rectangular Grid, 10 x 7. 193
Calendar. 194
5/8" Rectangular Grid, 10 x 10 195
1" Grid. 196
1/2" Grid 197
1/3" Grid 198
1/4" Grid 199
1/5" Grid 200
Unit Circle. 201
Unit Circle (2) 202
Unit Circle (6) 203
Circumference of a Circle marked for 100's 204
Circle marked for 3rds 205
Circle marked for 4ths 206
Circle marked for 5ths 207
Blank Number Line Continuum (4) 208
Blank Number Line Continuum (4) 20 Unit Markings 209
Celsius/Fahrenheit Thermometer, Freezing Point Indicated 210
4 Cup Measure – Marked for oz. and ml. 211
Quart and Liter – Marked for oz. and ml. 212
Three Pairs of 6-Inch/15-Centimeter Rulers. 213
Six 15-Centimeter Rulers 214
Protractor 0° to 180° Marked Right and Left Only 215
Standard Protractor 216

Name: ____________________

Name: ____________________

EXPERT
KNOWLEDGE

USEFUL
KNOWLEDGE

ESSENTIAL
KNOWLEDGE

Name: ______________________________

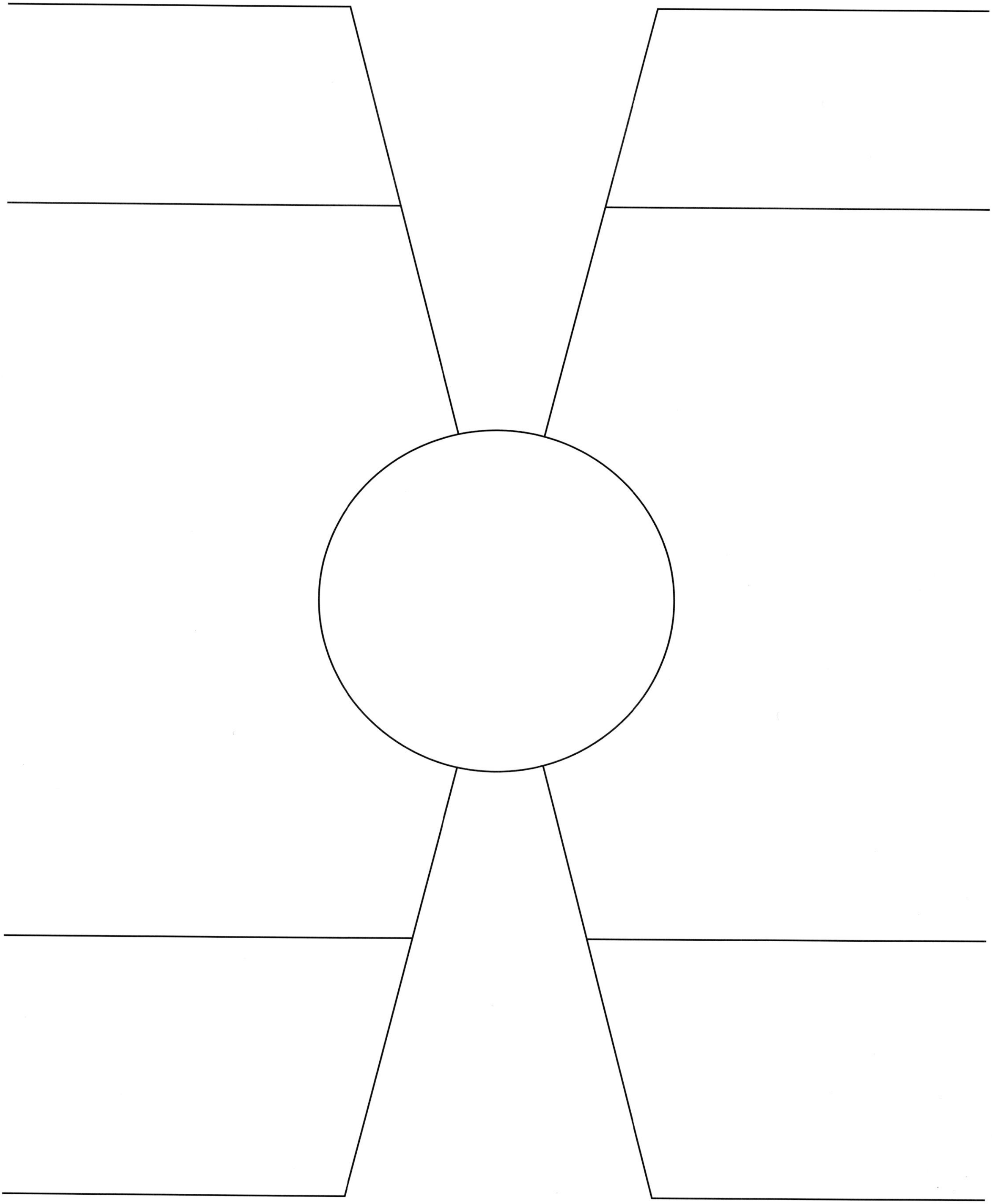

Name: ______________________________

Concept:	Challenges:	Evidence:	Understanding:
	Information:	Evidence:	

Name: ______________________________

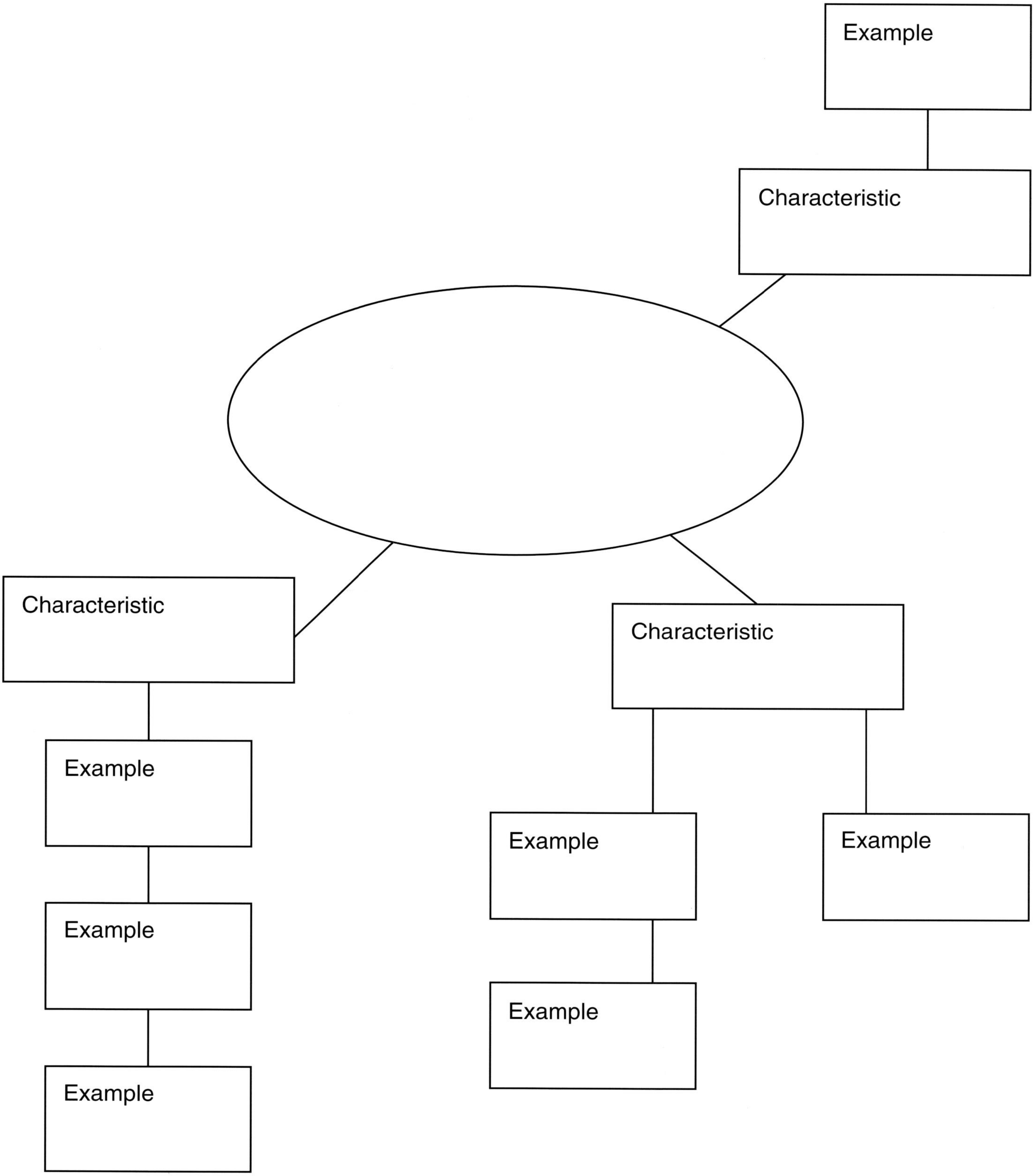
Example
Characteristic
Characteristic
Characteristic
Example
Example
Example
Example
Example
Example

Name: ______________________________

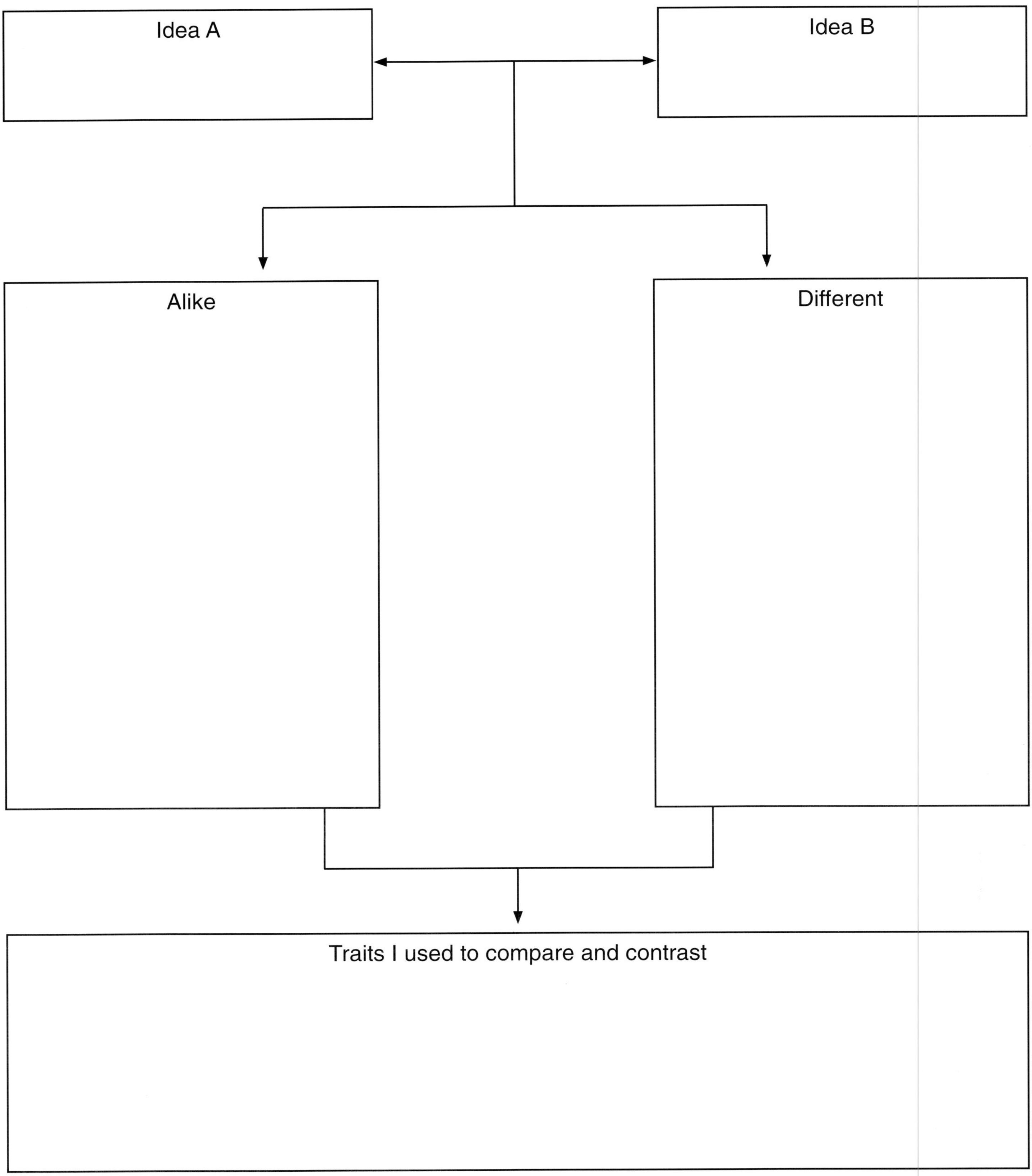
Idea A
Idea B
Alike
Different
Traits I used to compare and contrast

Name: ____________________

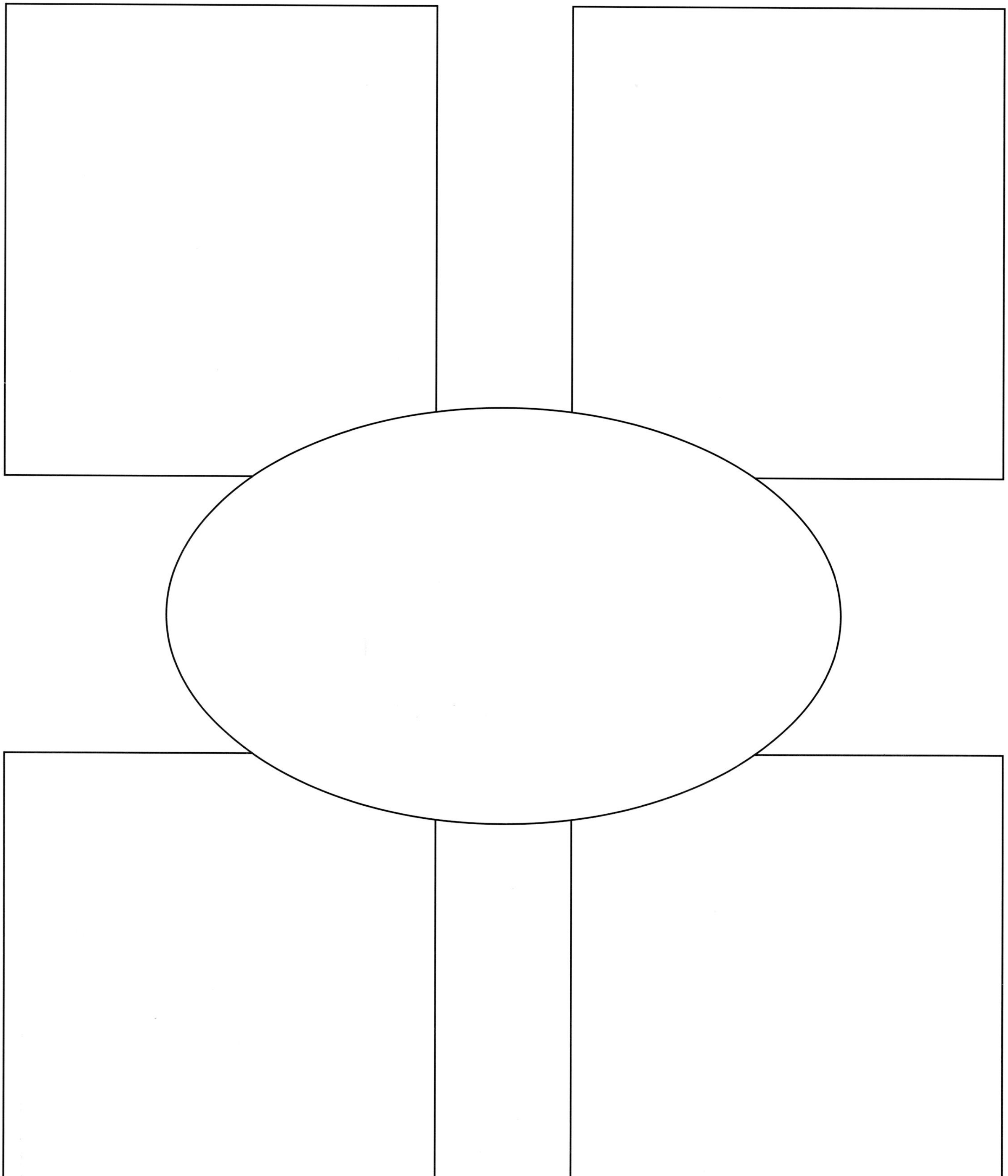

Name: ________________________________

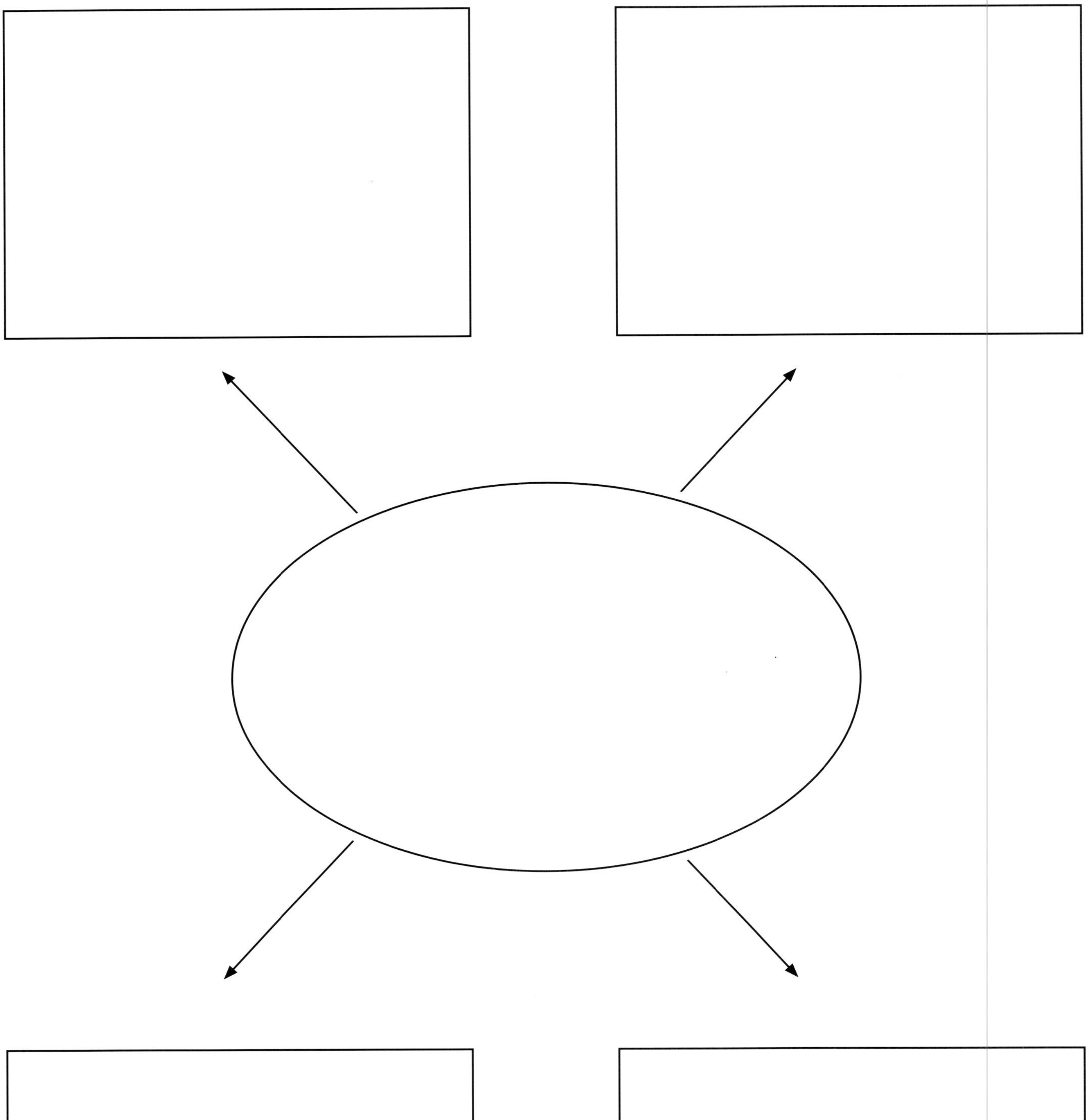

Name: ______________________________

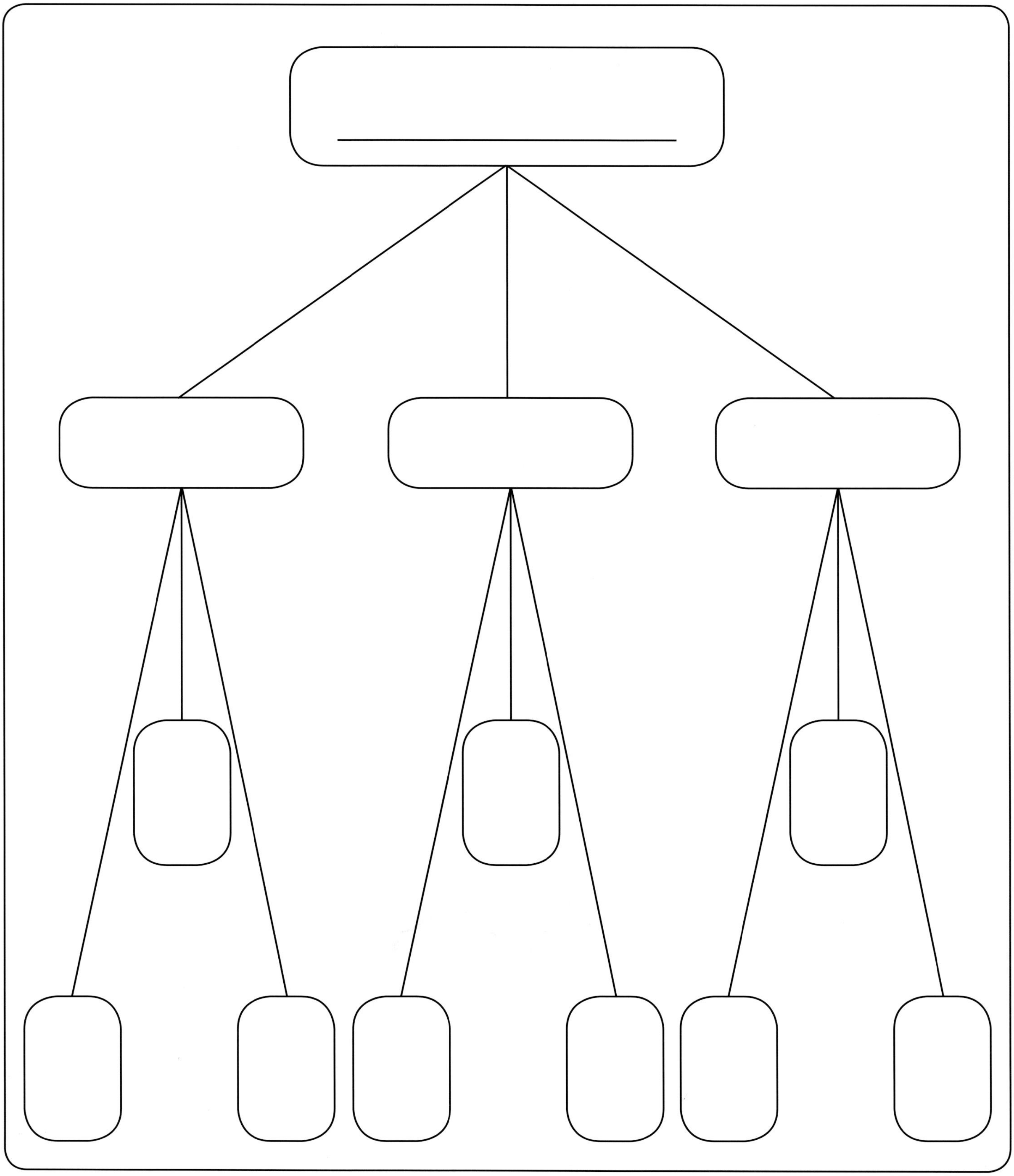

Name: ______________________________

Name: ______________________________

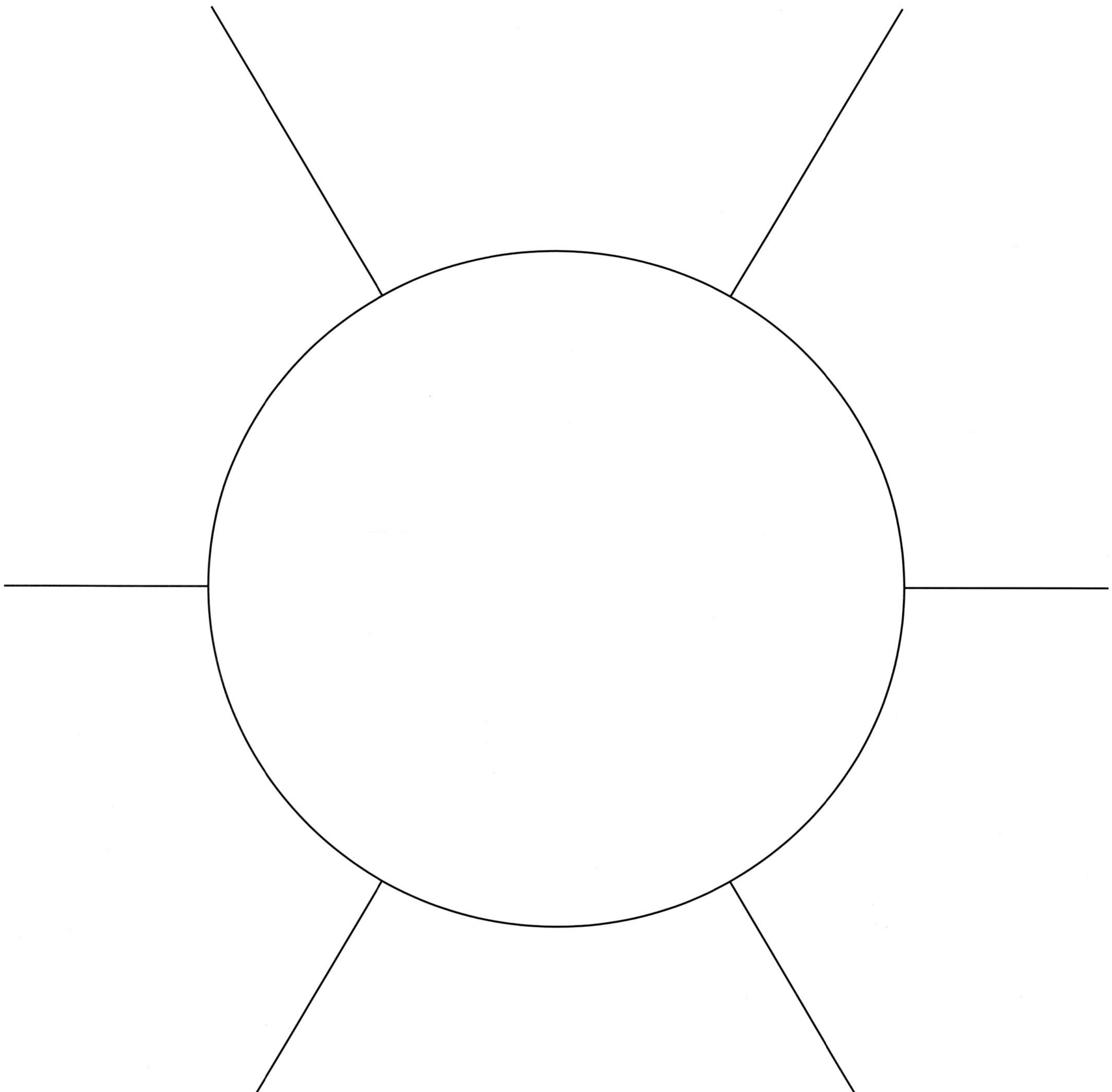

Name: ____________________

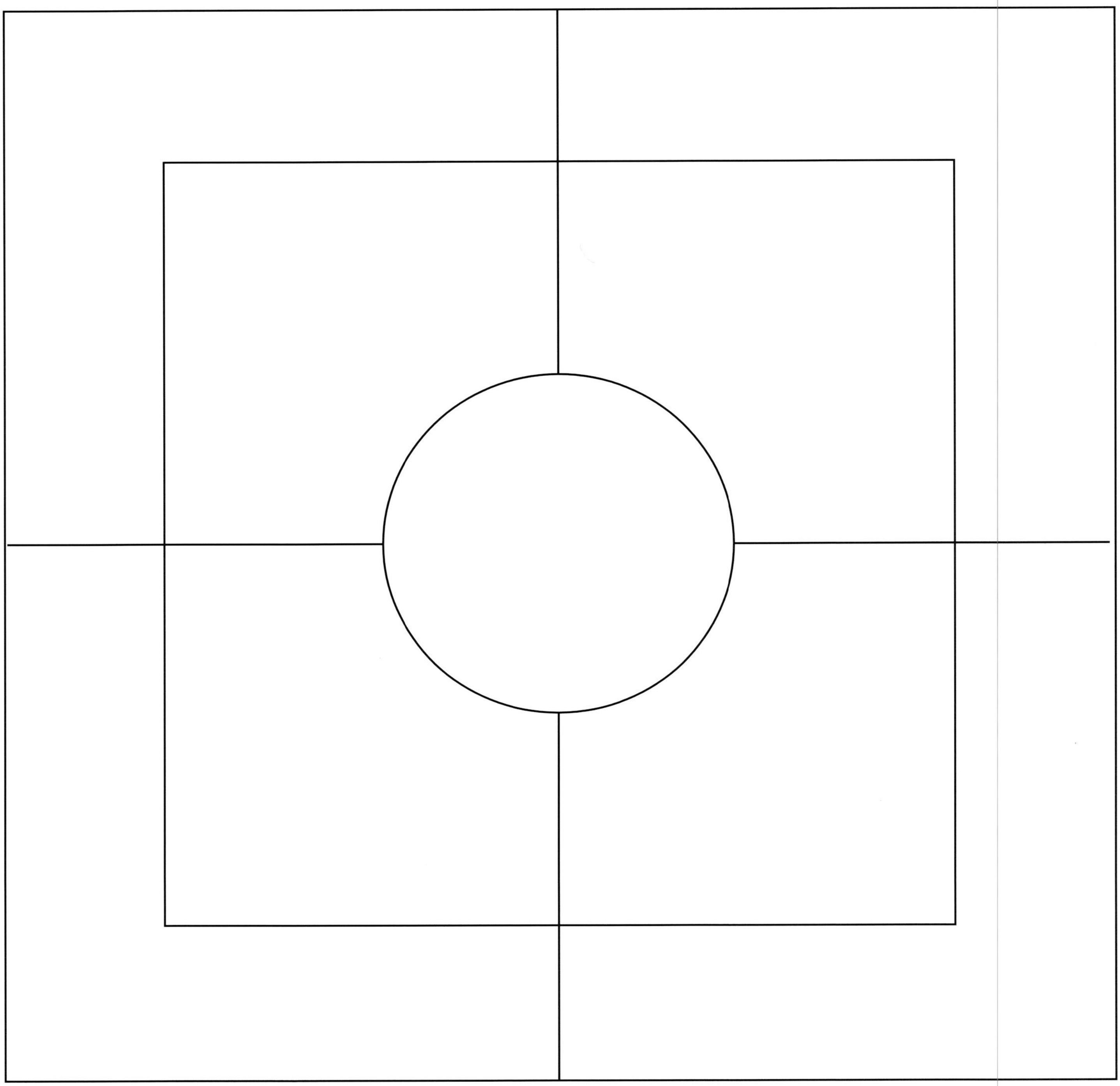

Name: ______________________________

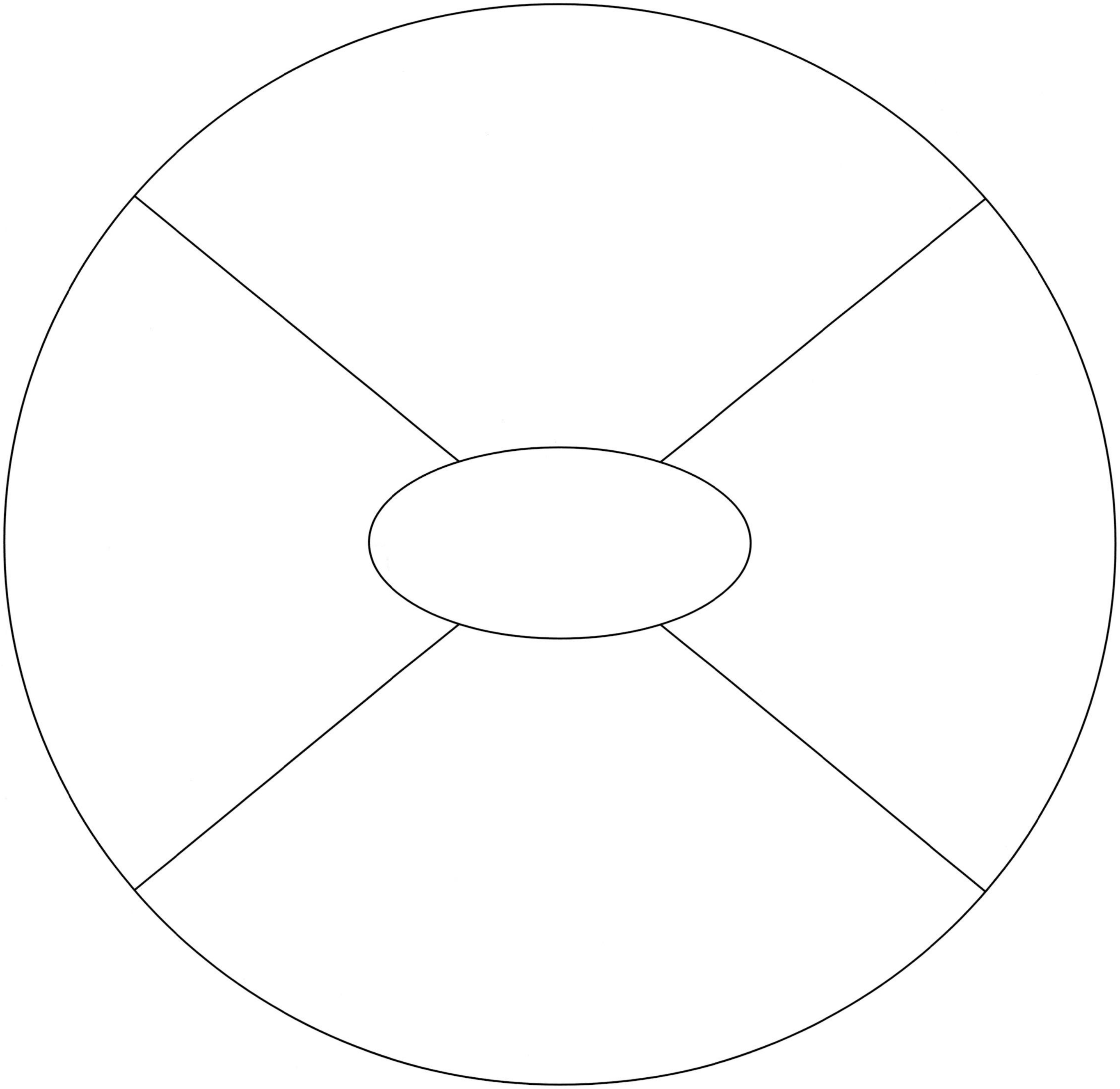

Name: ______________________________

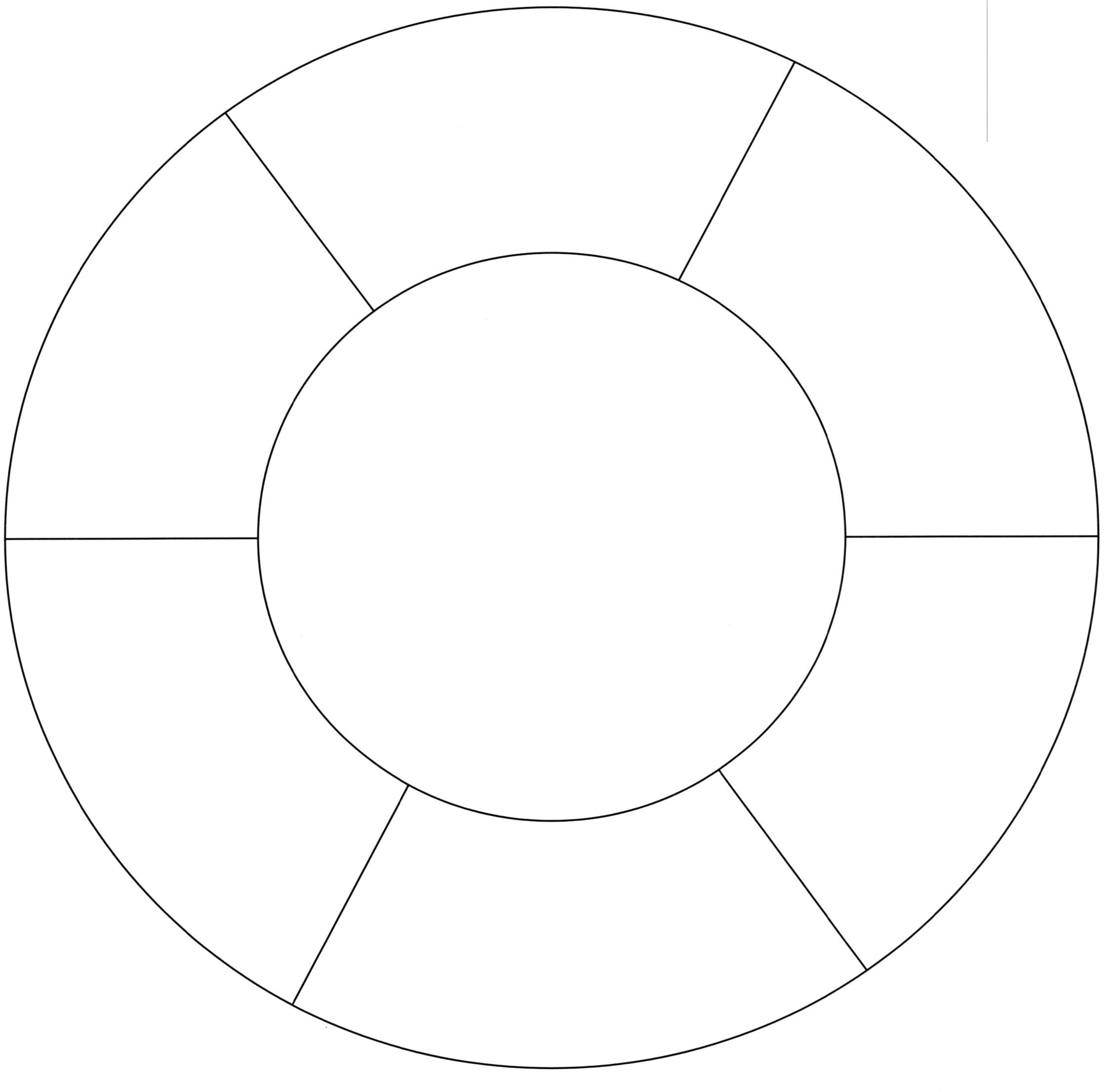

Name: ____________________

Definition in own words:

Examples

Concept

Non-Examples

Characteristics:

Name: ____________________

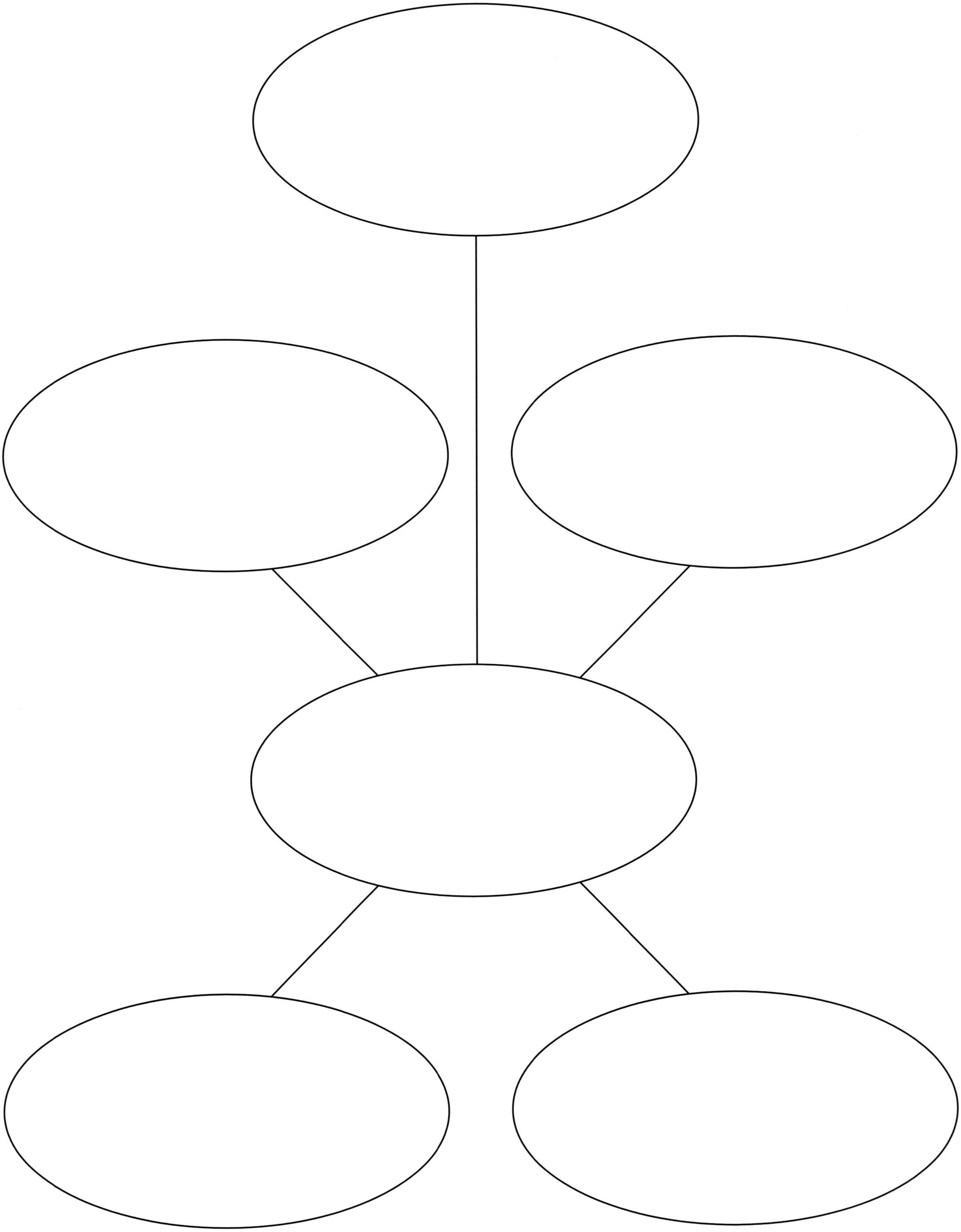

Name: ____________________

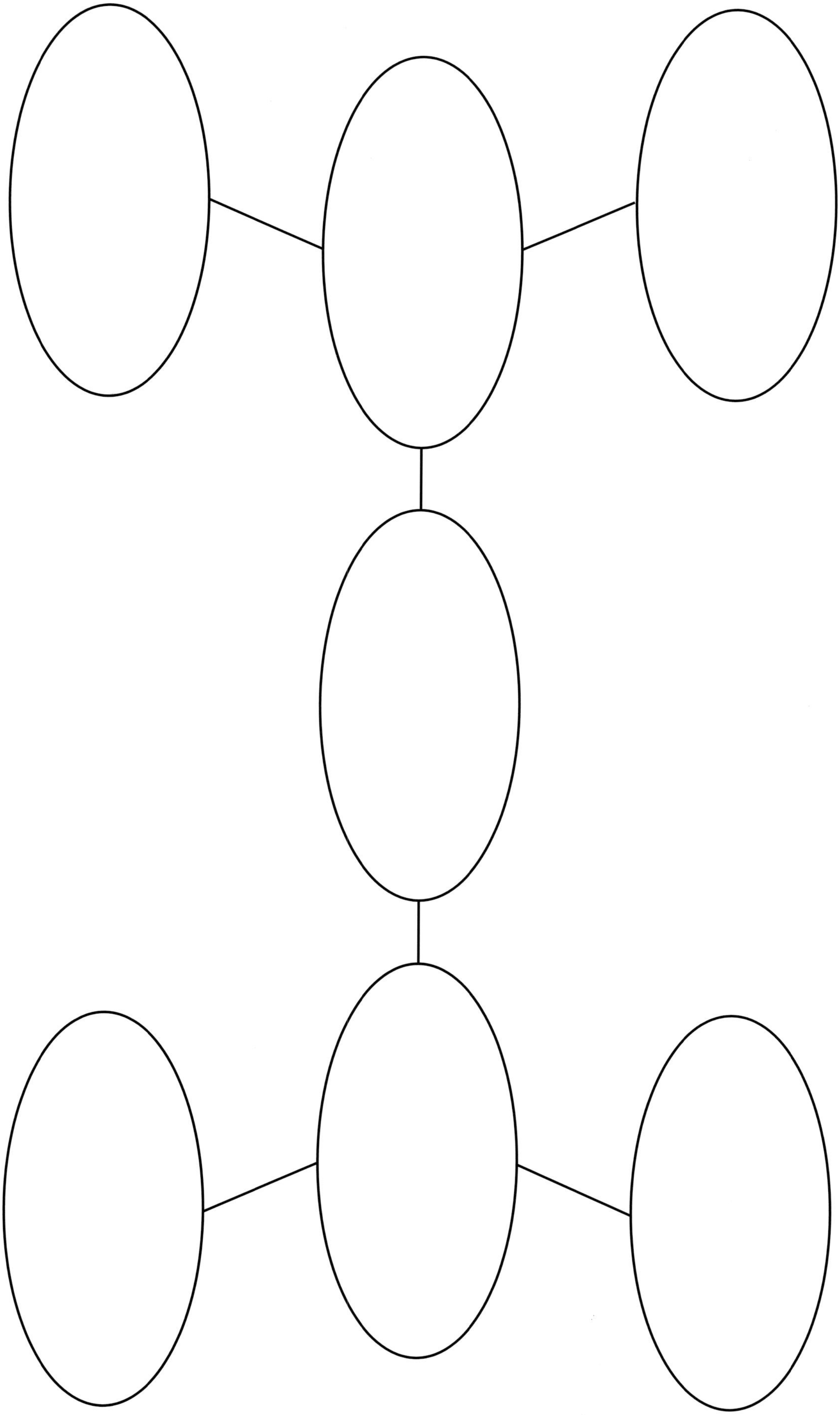

Name: ______________________________

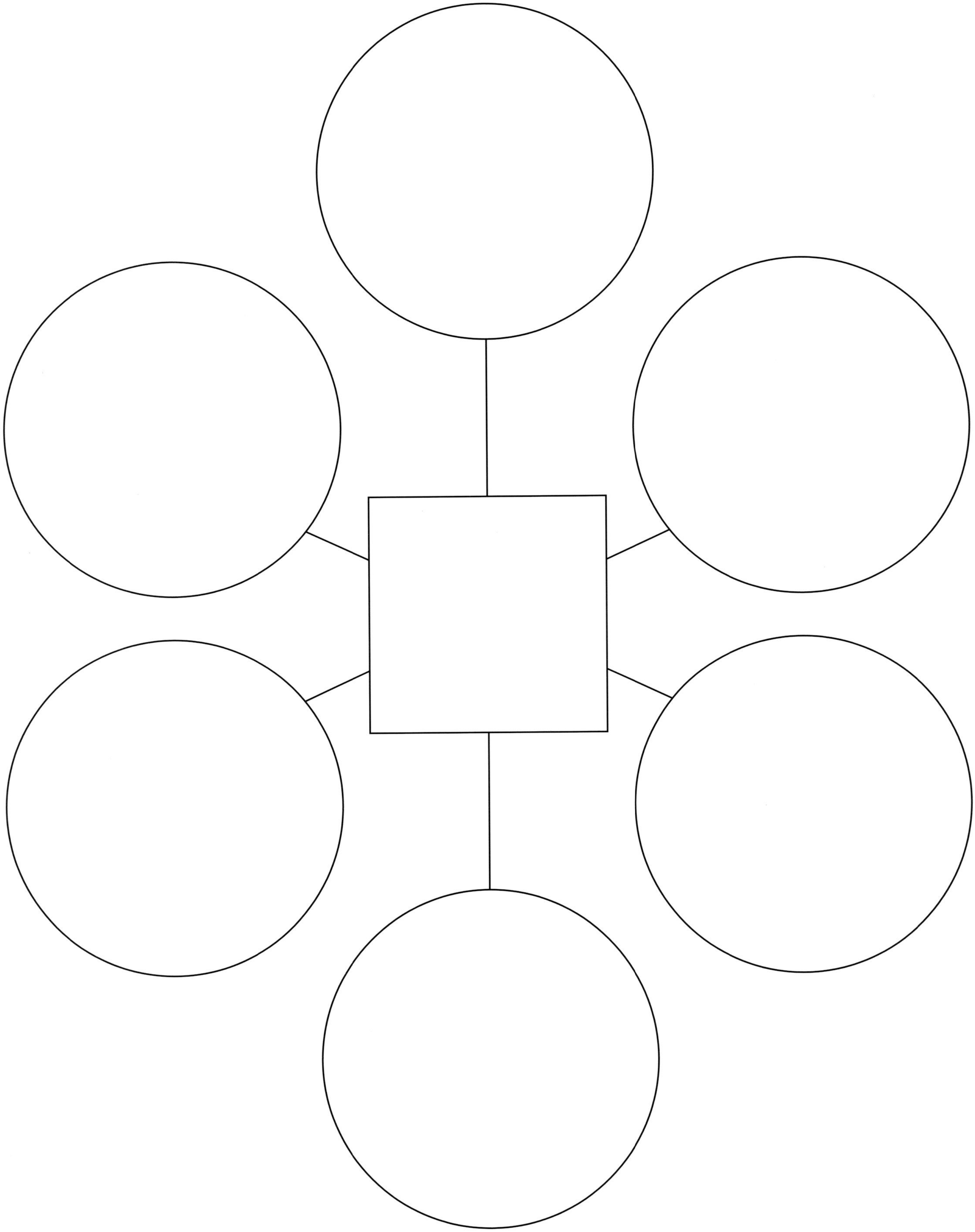

Name: ______________________________

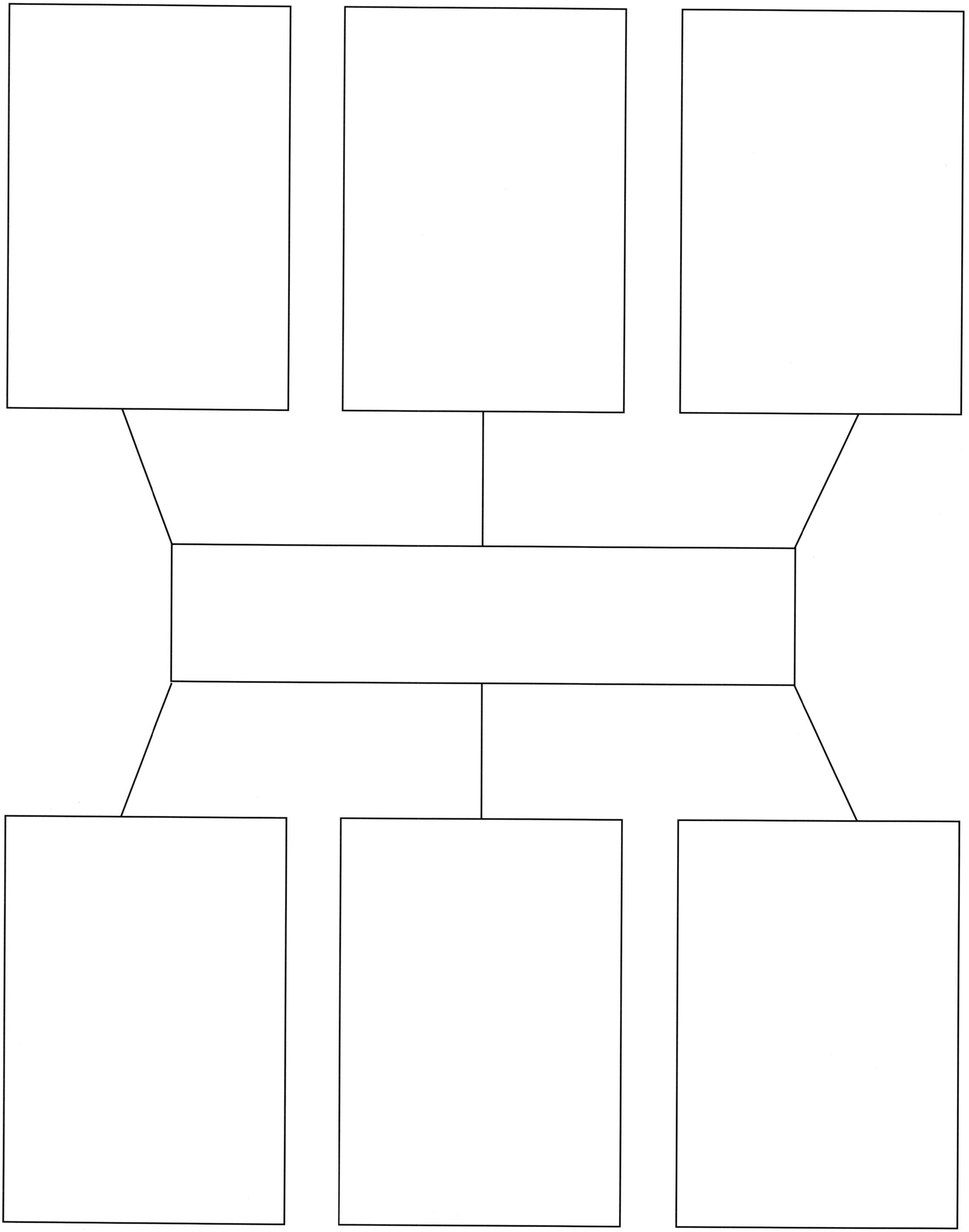

Name: ______________________________

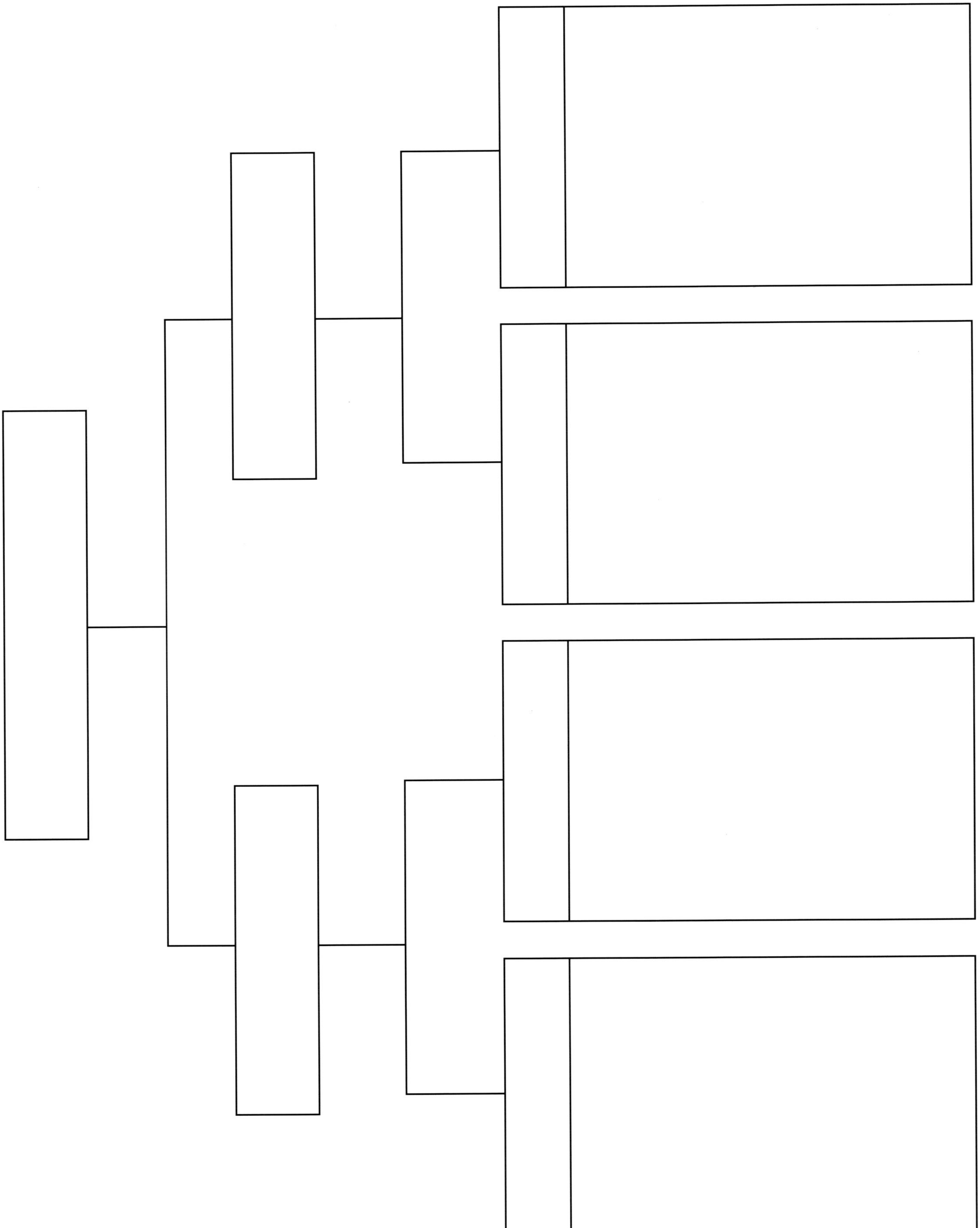

Name: ______________________________

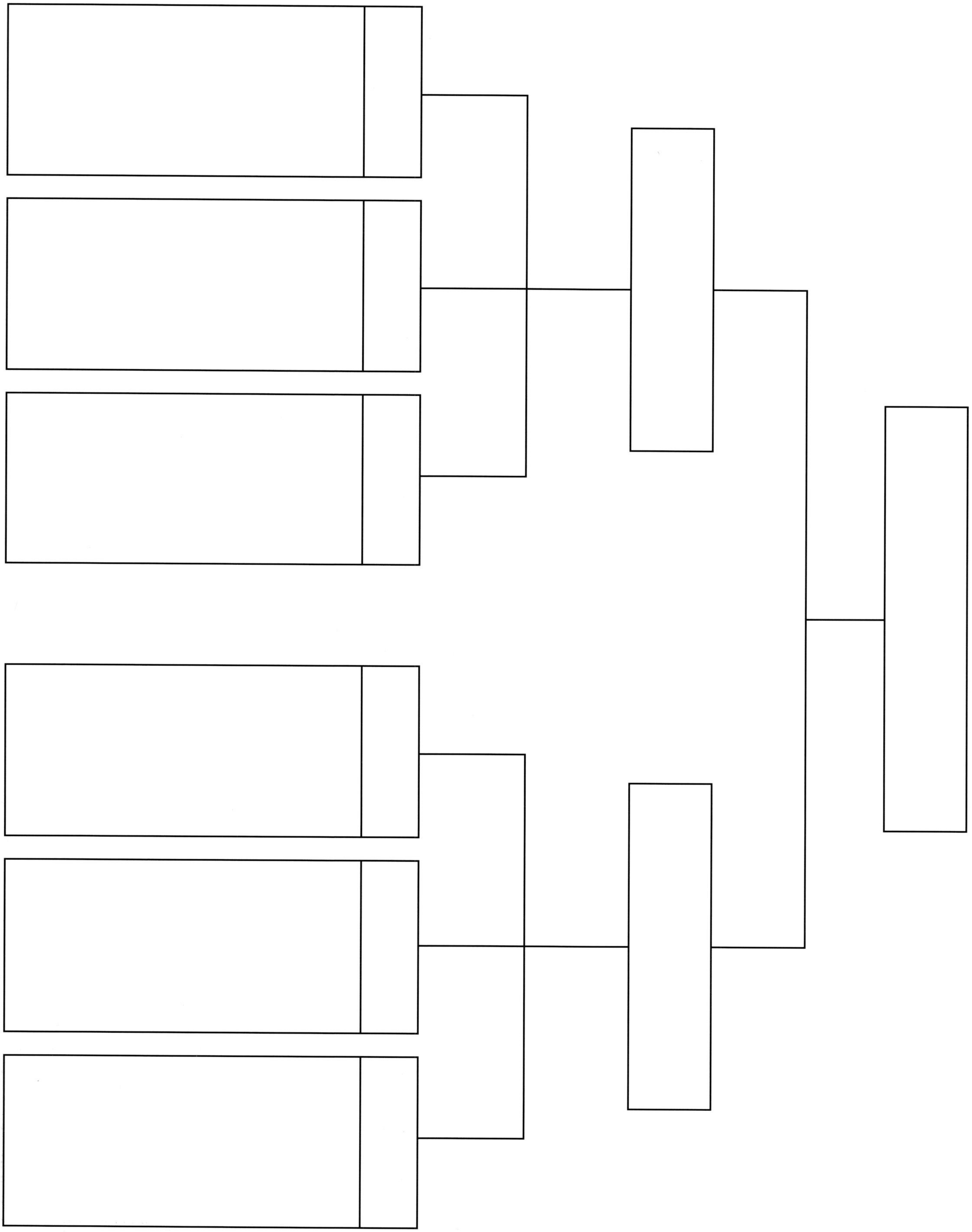

Name: ____________________

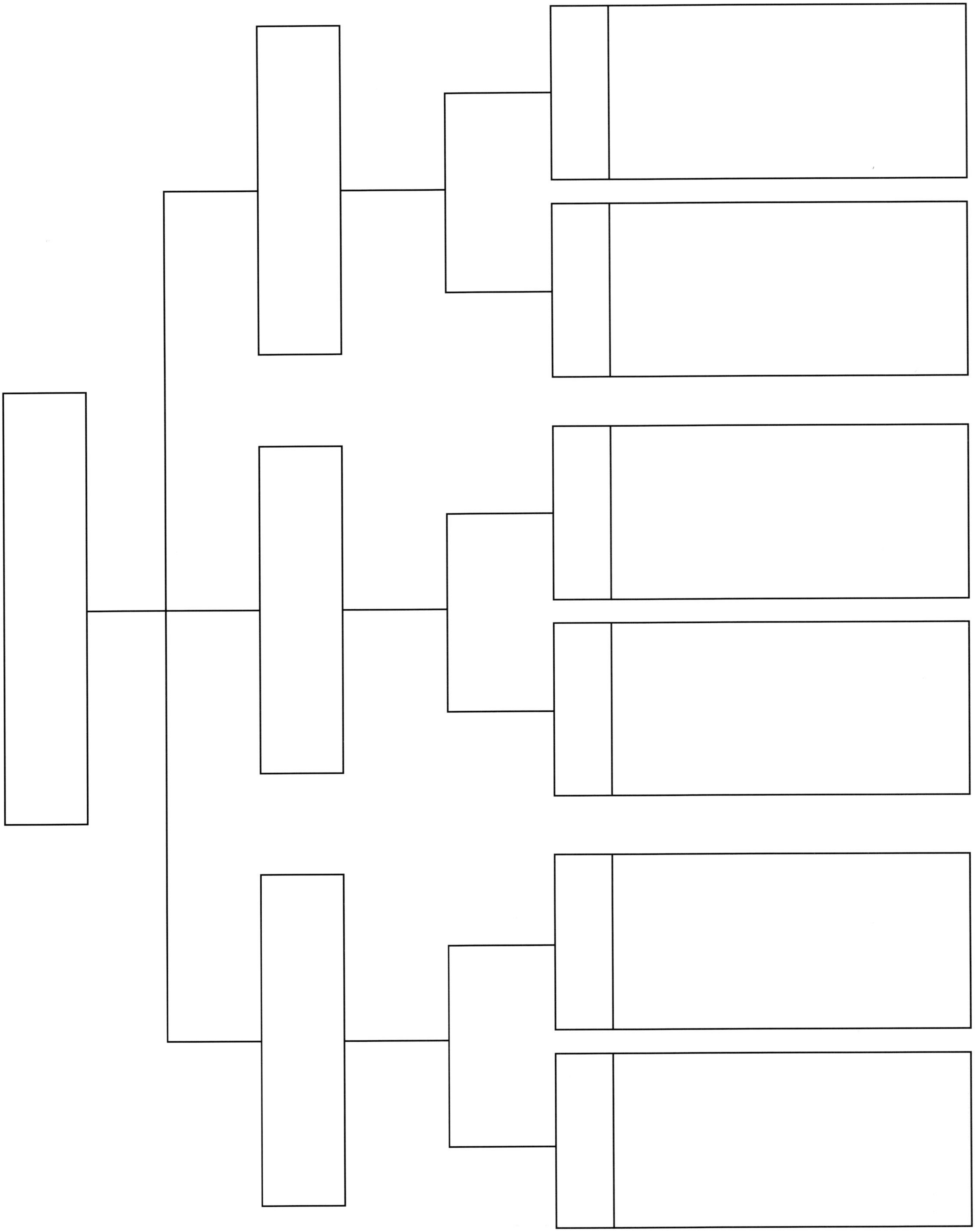

Name: ____________________

Name: ____________________

Name: ______________________________

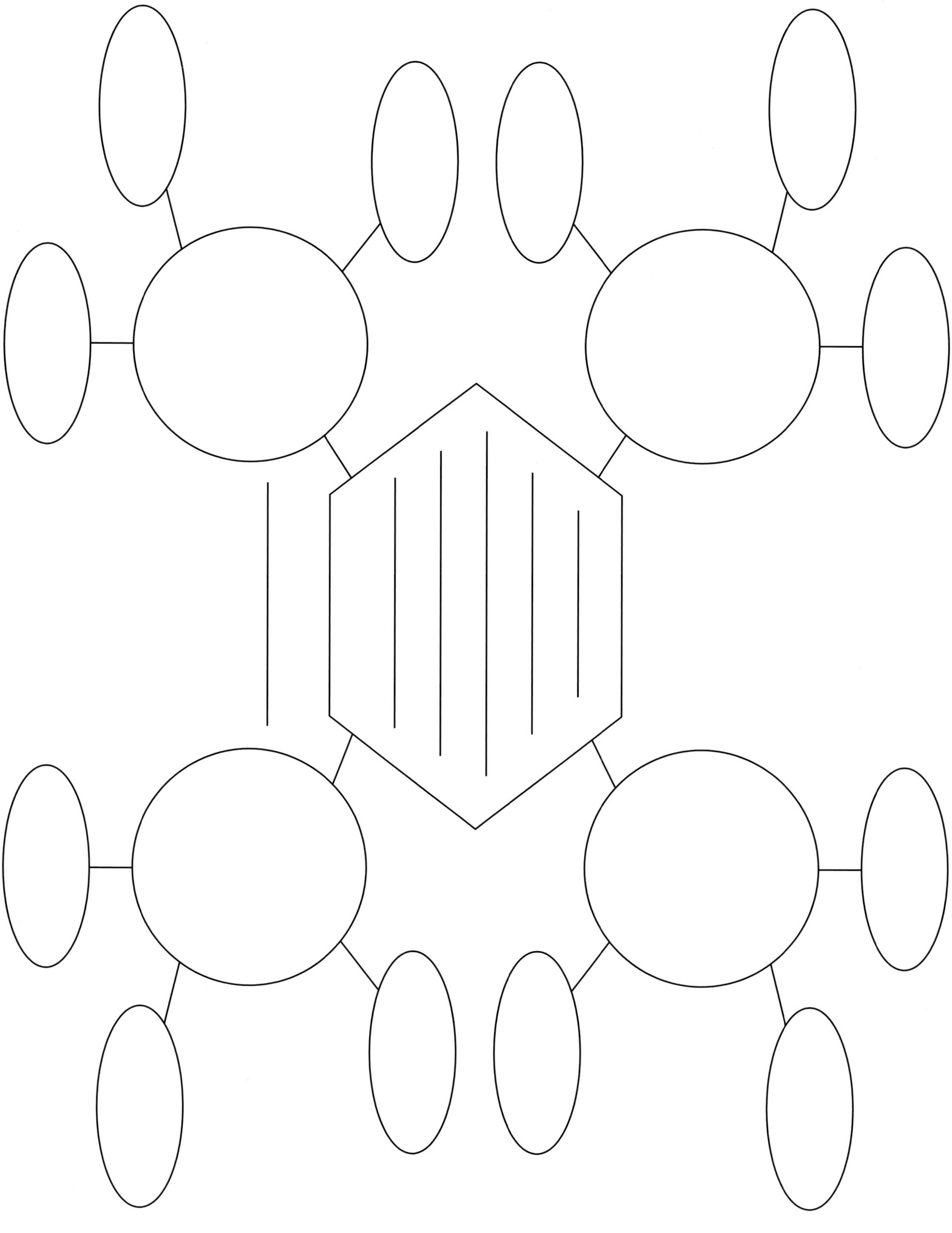

Name: ____________________

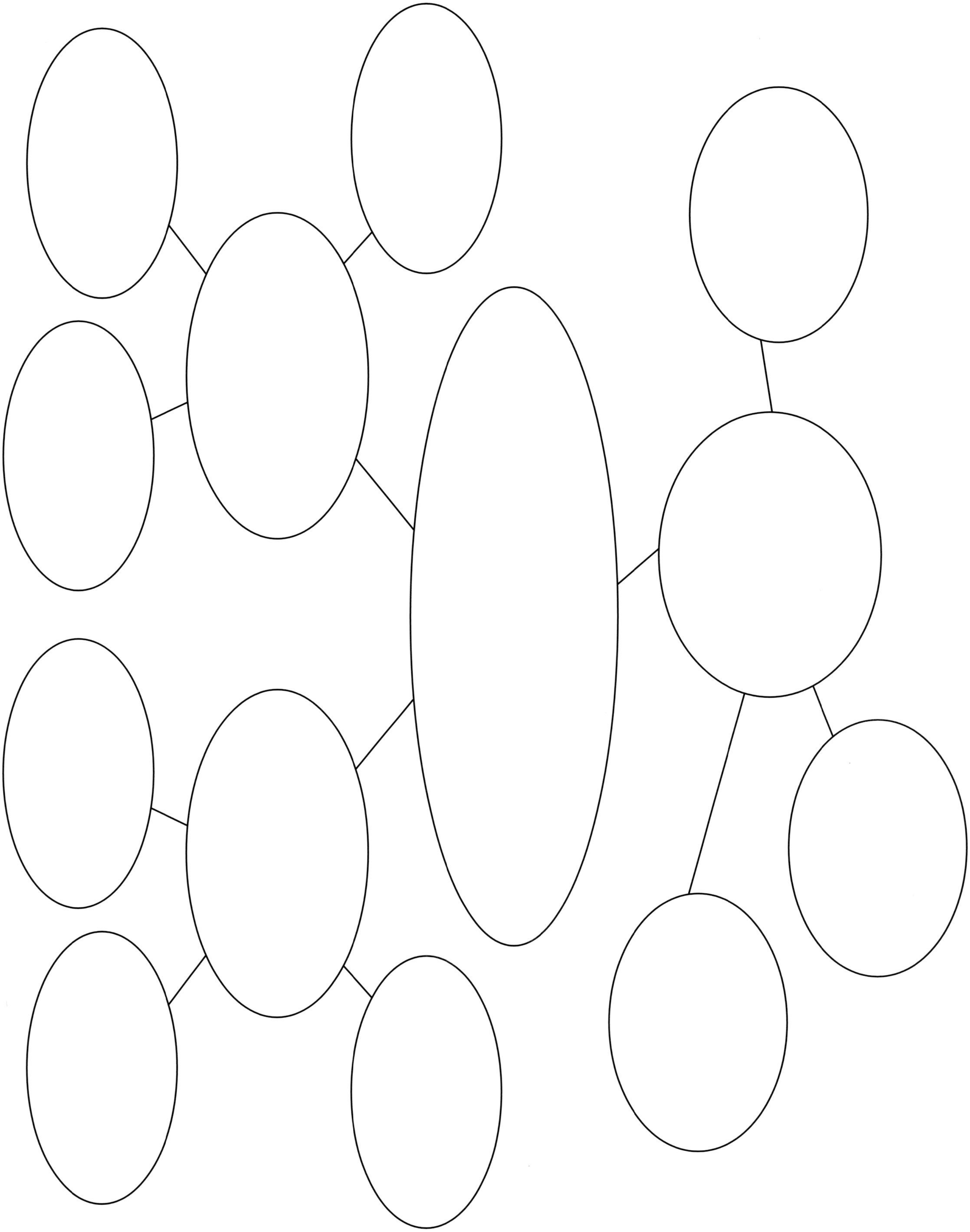

Name: ____________________

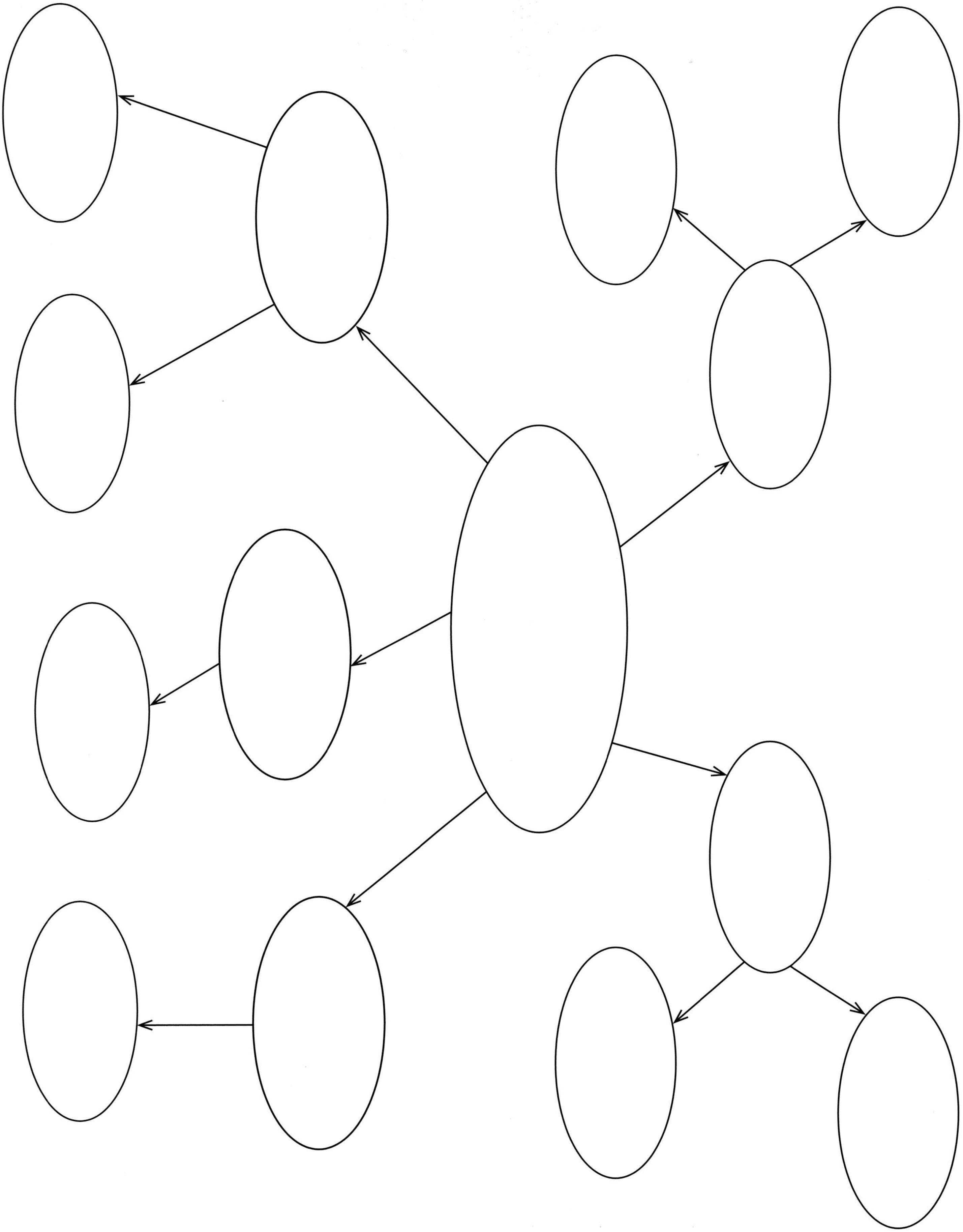

Name: ____________________

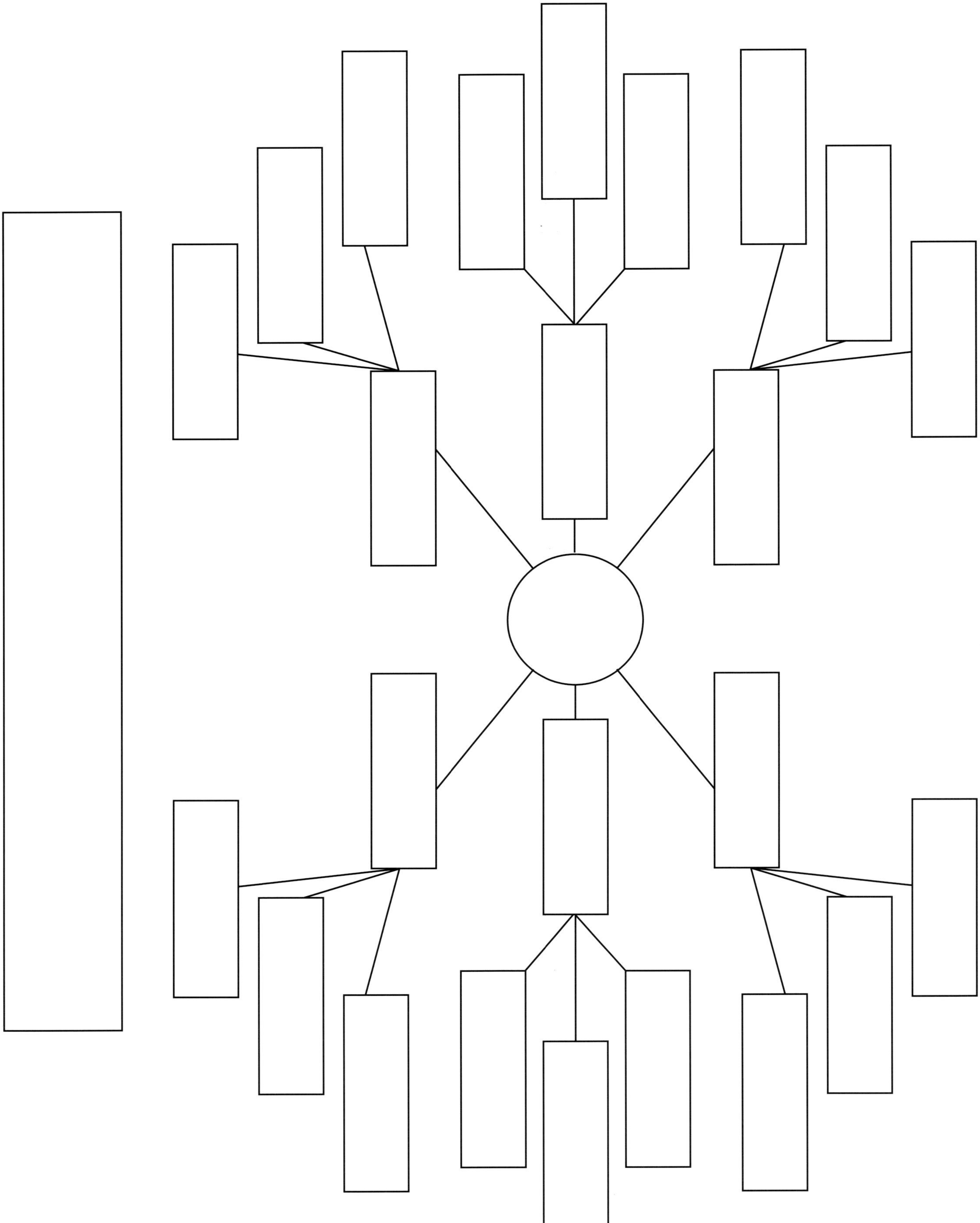

Name: ____________________

Topic: ____________________

A	B	C	D
E	F	G	H
I	J	K	L
M	N	O	P
Q	R	S	T
U	V	W	XYZ

Name: ____________________

Name: ____________________

Definition (in your own words):	Facts/Characteristics:
Examples:	Non-Examples:

Used with permission from Frayer, D. A., Fredrick, W. C., & Klausmeier, H. J. (1969). *A schema for testing the level of concept mastery* (Working Paper No. 16). Madison, WI: Wisconsin Research and Development Center for Cognitive Learning.

Name: ______________________________

Definition		Characteristics
	Word	
Examples		Non-Examples

Used with permission from Frayer, D. A., Fredrick, W. C., & Klausmeier, H. J. (1969). *A schema for testing the level of concept mastery* (Working Paper No. 16). Madison, WI: Wisconsin Research and Development Center for Cognitive Learning.

Name: ____________________

Vocabulary Word	My Knowledge of the Word Rating 1–5.	My Own Definition	Dictionary Definition

Name: ______________________

Word

Visual

Definition in my own words: ______________________

My first sentence:

____

____

____

____

Dictionary definition:

____

____

____

My second sentence:

____

____

____

____

Name: ____________________

A

B

is to

As

C

D

is to

Name: ______________________________

What is it?

Definition:

Examples

Non-Examples

Word

Illustration

Name: ______________________________

What is it?

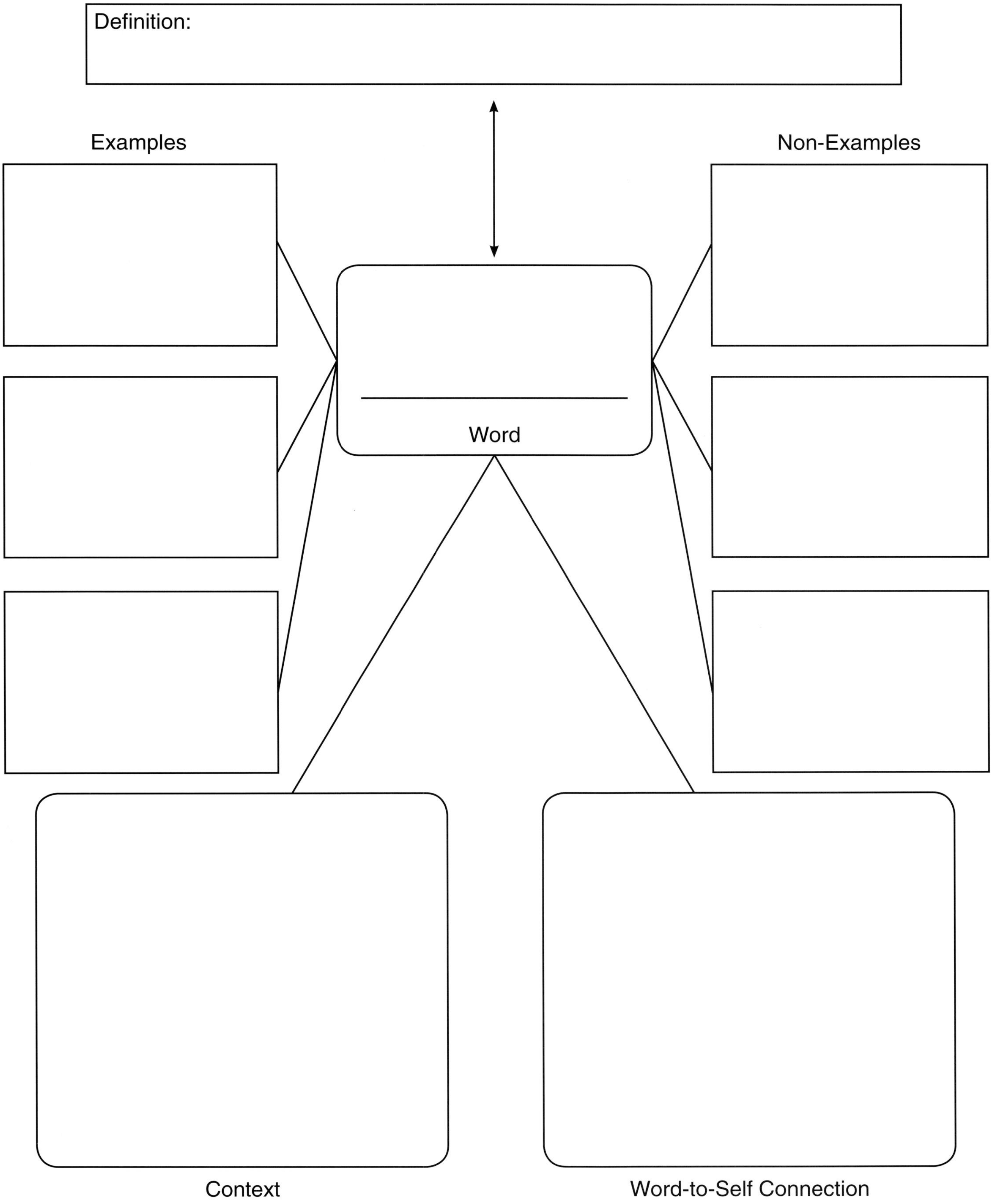

Name: ______________________________

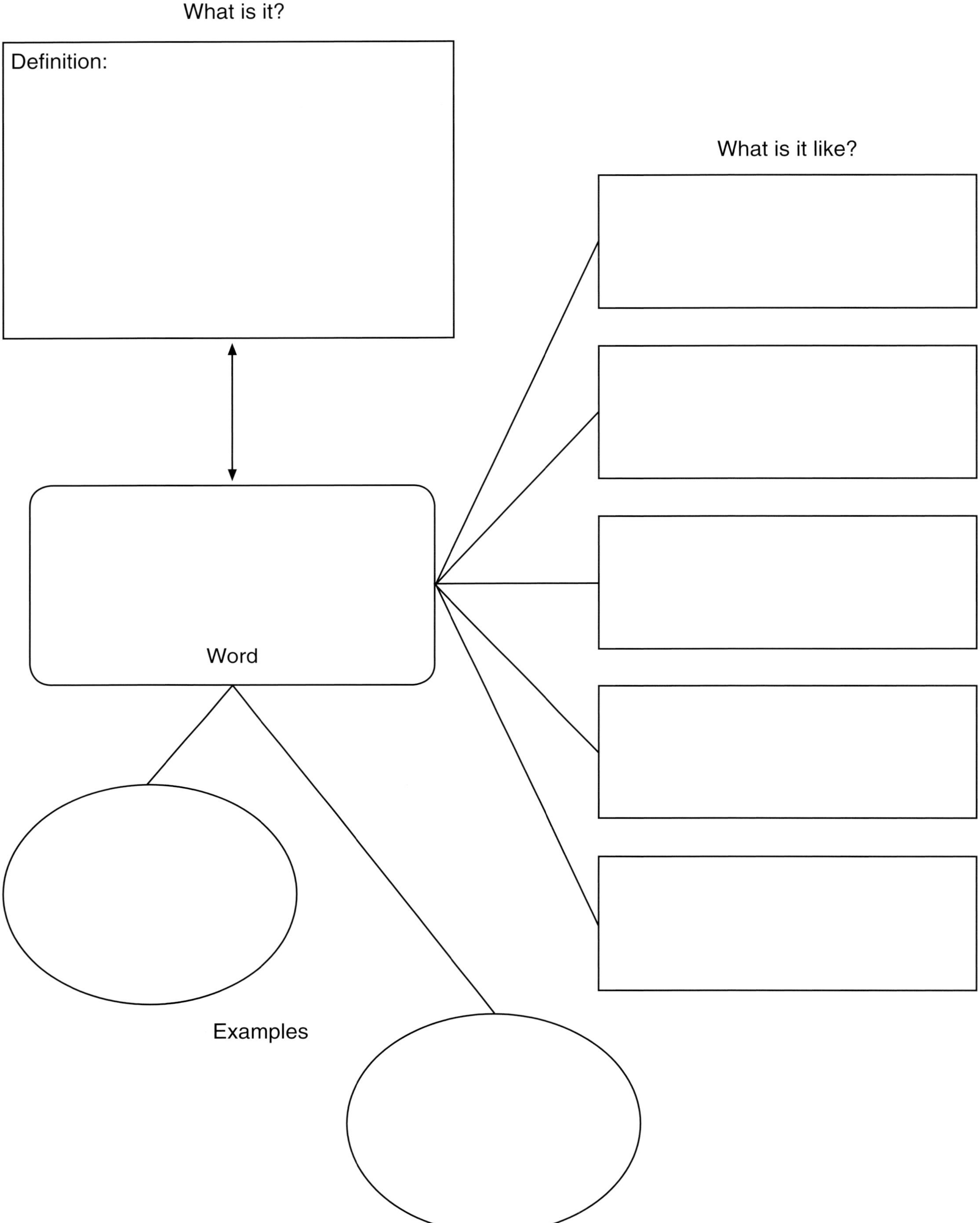

Name: ______________________________

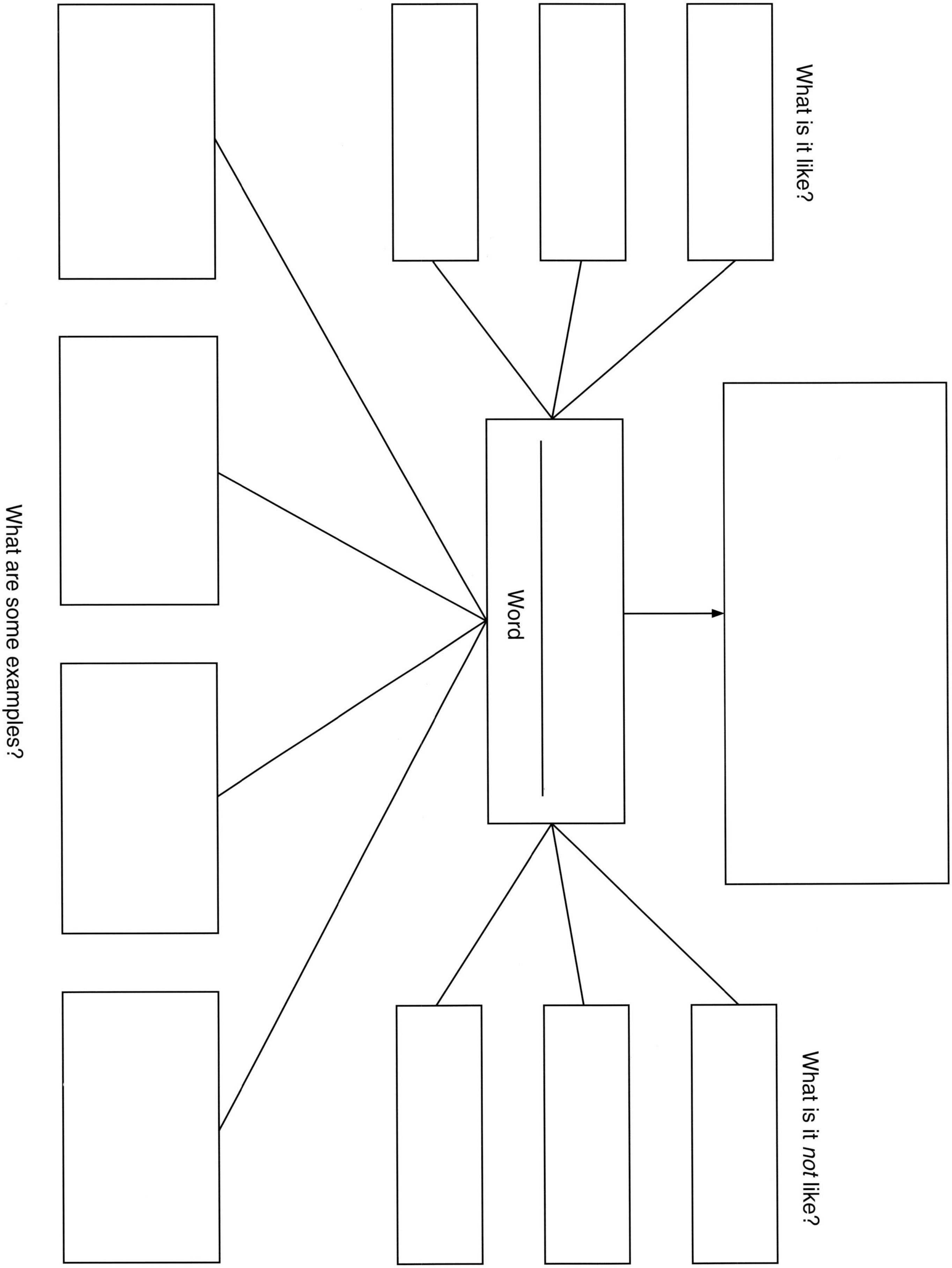
What is it like?
Word
What is it?
What are some examples?
What is it *not* like?

Name: ______________________________

Name: ______________________________

Name: ________________________________

Name: ____________________

A.

B.

Name: ______________________________

Sketch:

Written description:

Name: ______________________

Item:

Properties:

1.

2.

3.

4.

Name: ____________________

A.

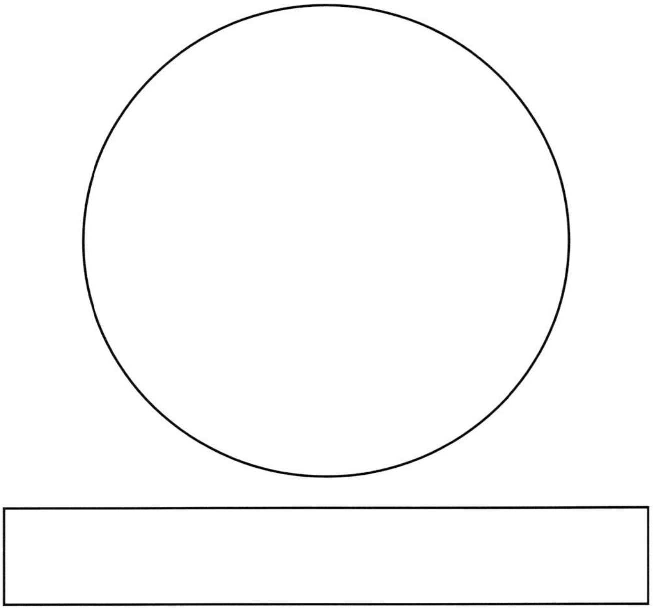

B.

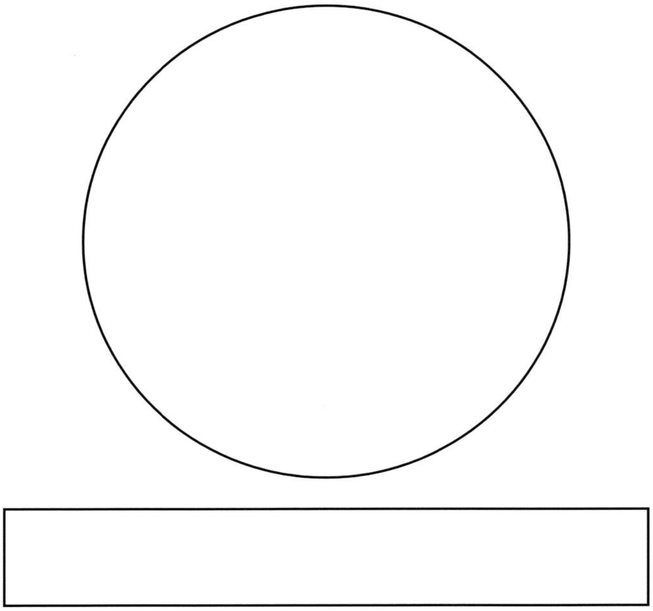

C.

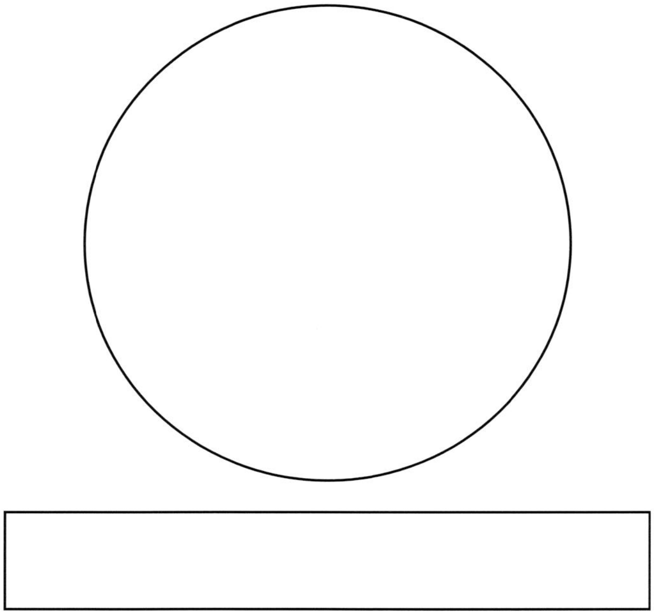

D.

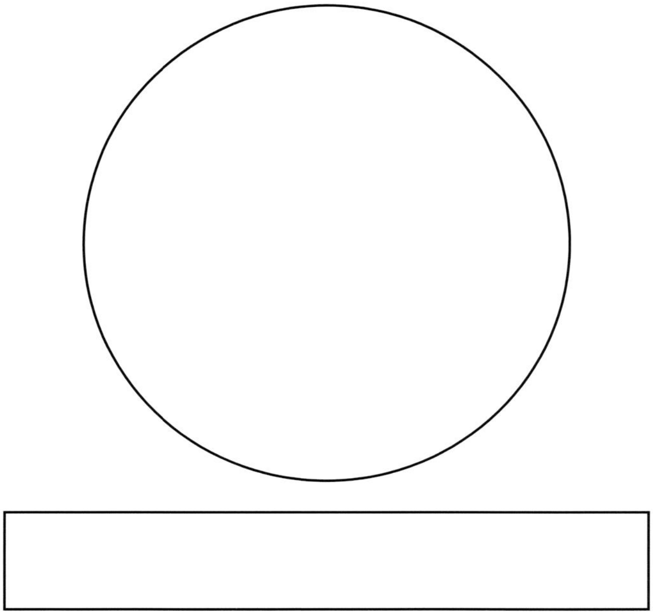

Name: ____________________

A.

B.

C.

D.

Name: ____________________

A.

B.

C.

D.

E.

F.

Name: ______________________

Name: ____________________

____

Name: ____________________

1. ____________________

2. ____________________

3. ____________________

4. ____________________

1. ____________________

2. ____________________

3. ____________________

4. ____________________

1. ____________________

2. ____________________

3. ____________________

4. ____________________

1. ____________________

2. ____________________

3. ____________________

4. ____________________

Name: ______________________________

1. ______________________________

2. ______________________________

3. ______________________________

1. ______________________________

2. ______________________________

3. ______________________________

Name: ______________________________

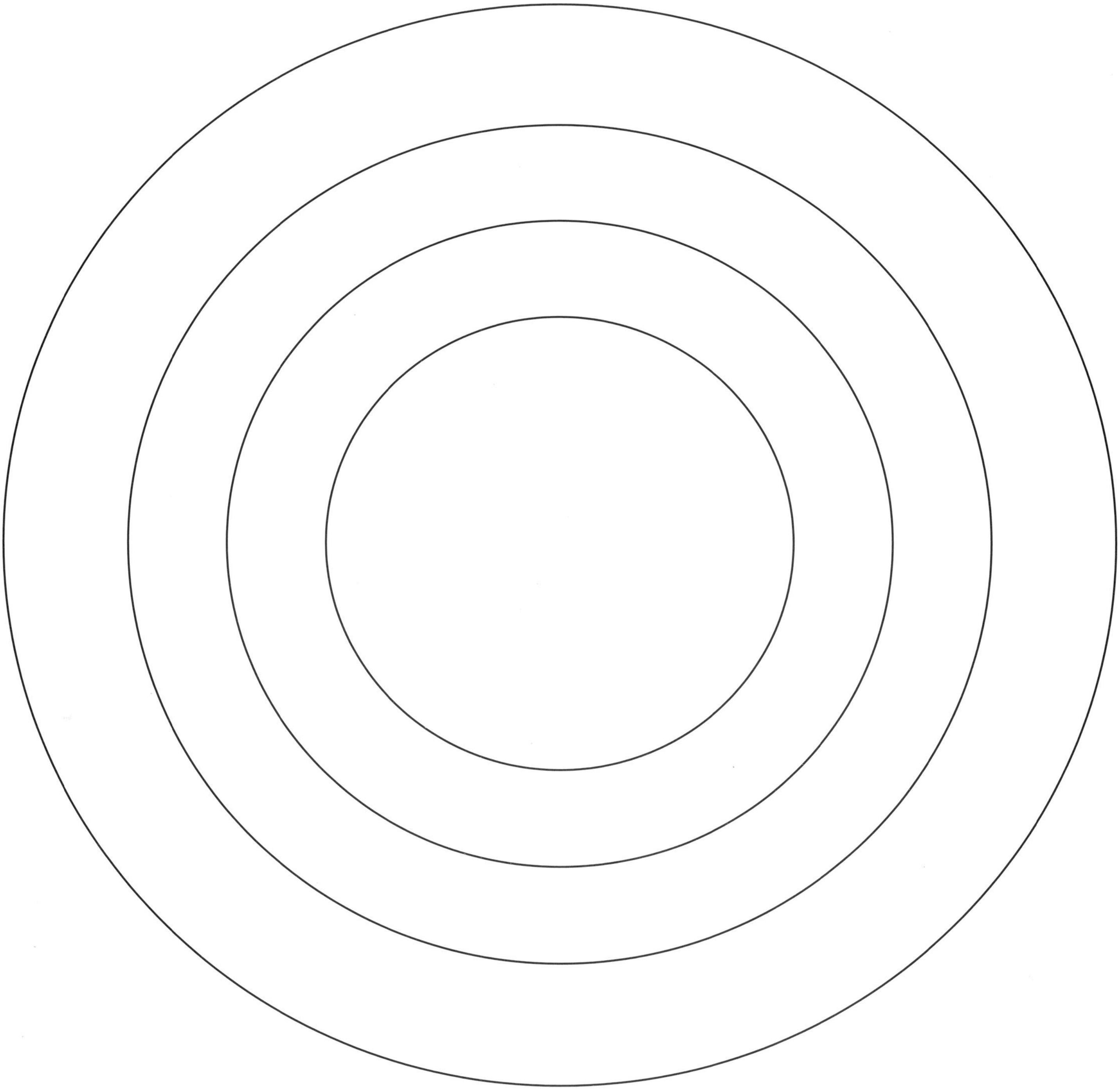

Name: ____________________________

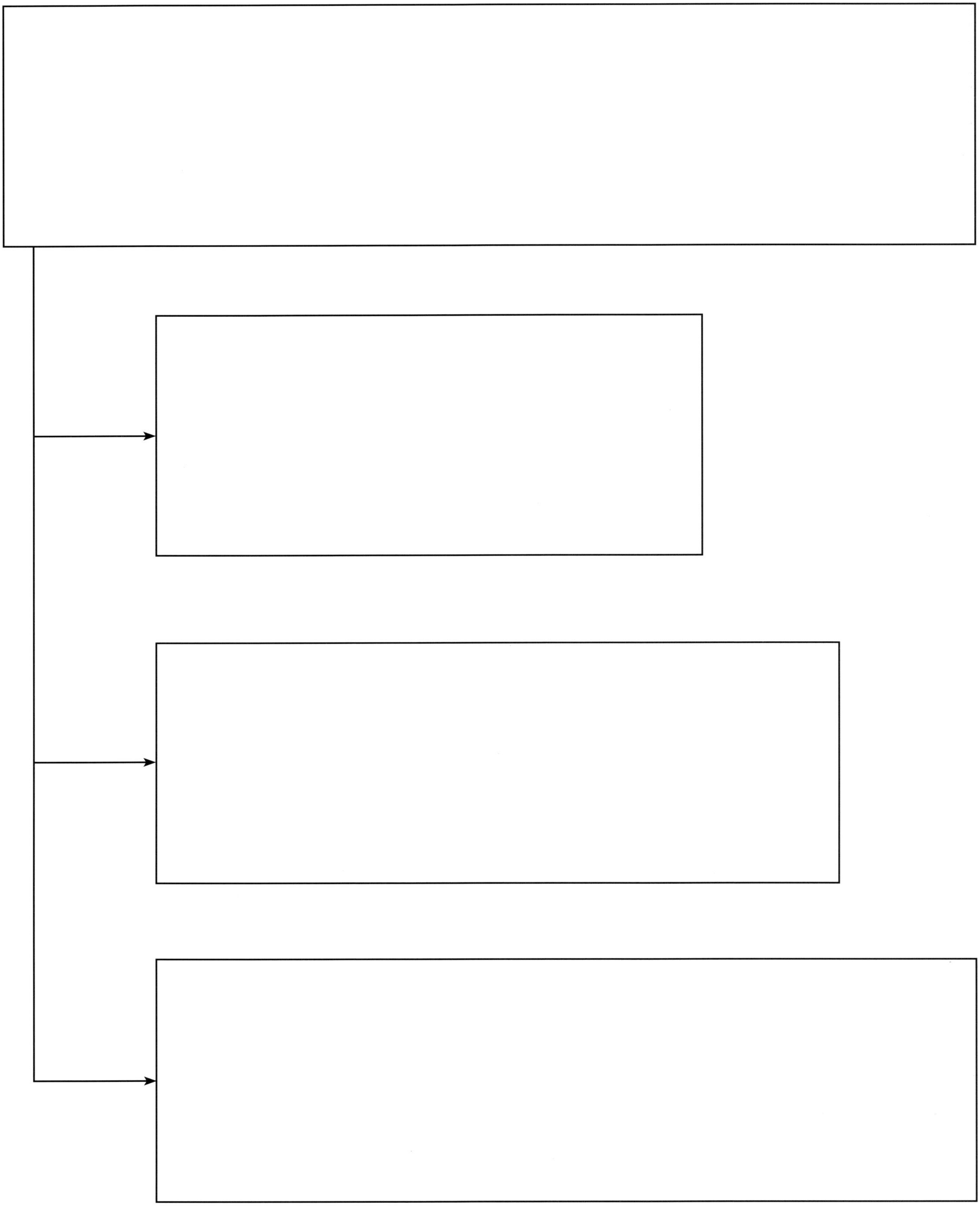

Name: ____________________

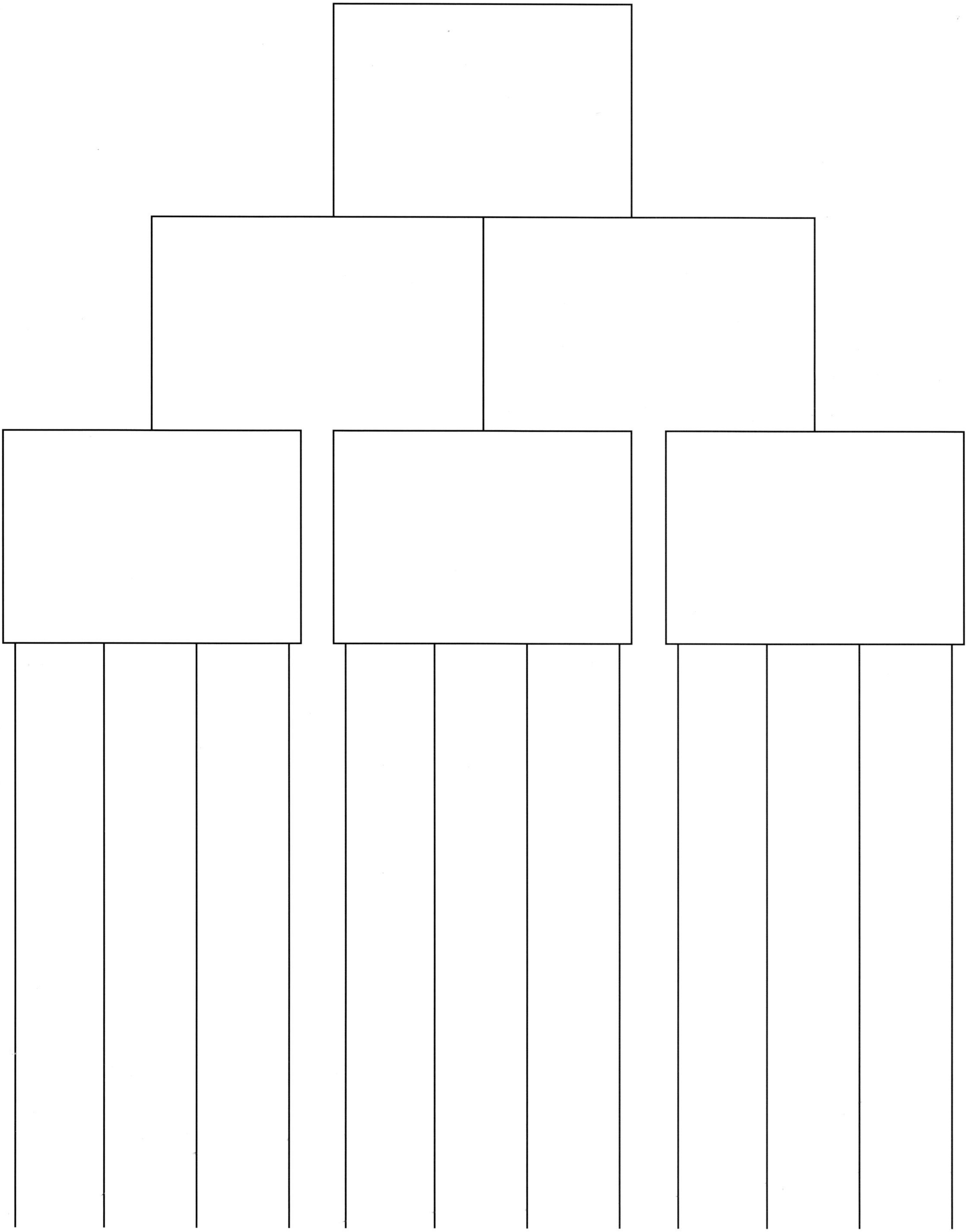

Name: ______________________________

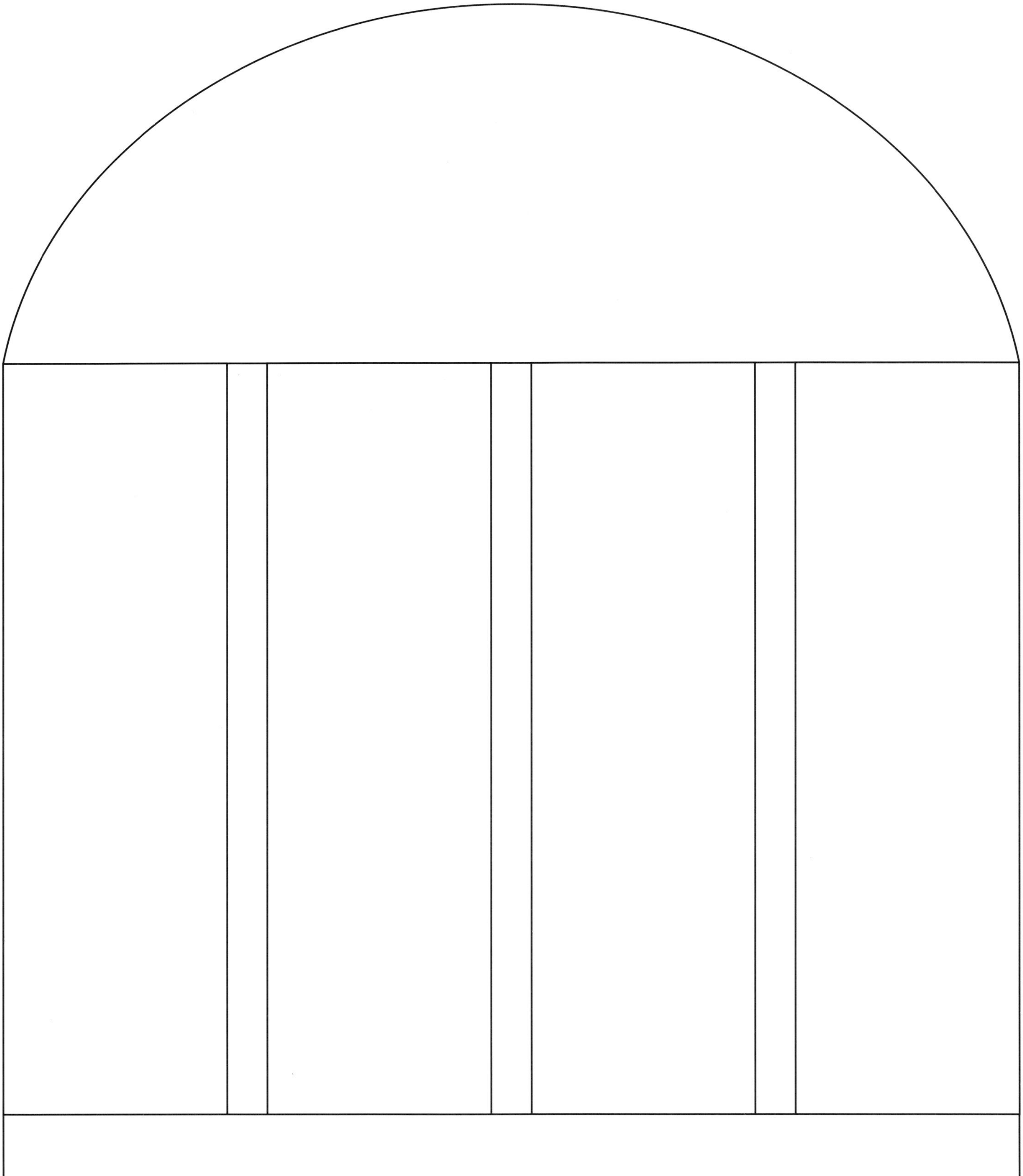

Name: ______________________________

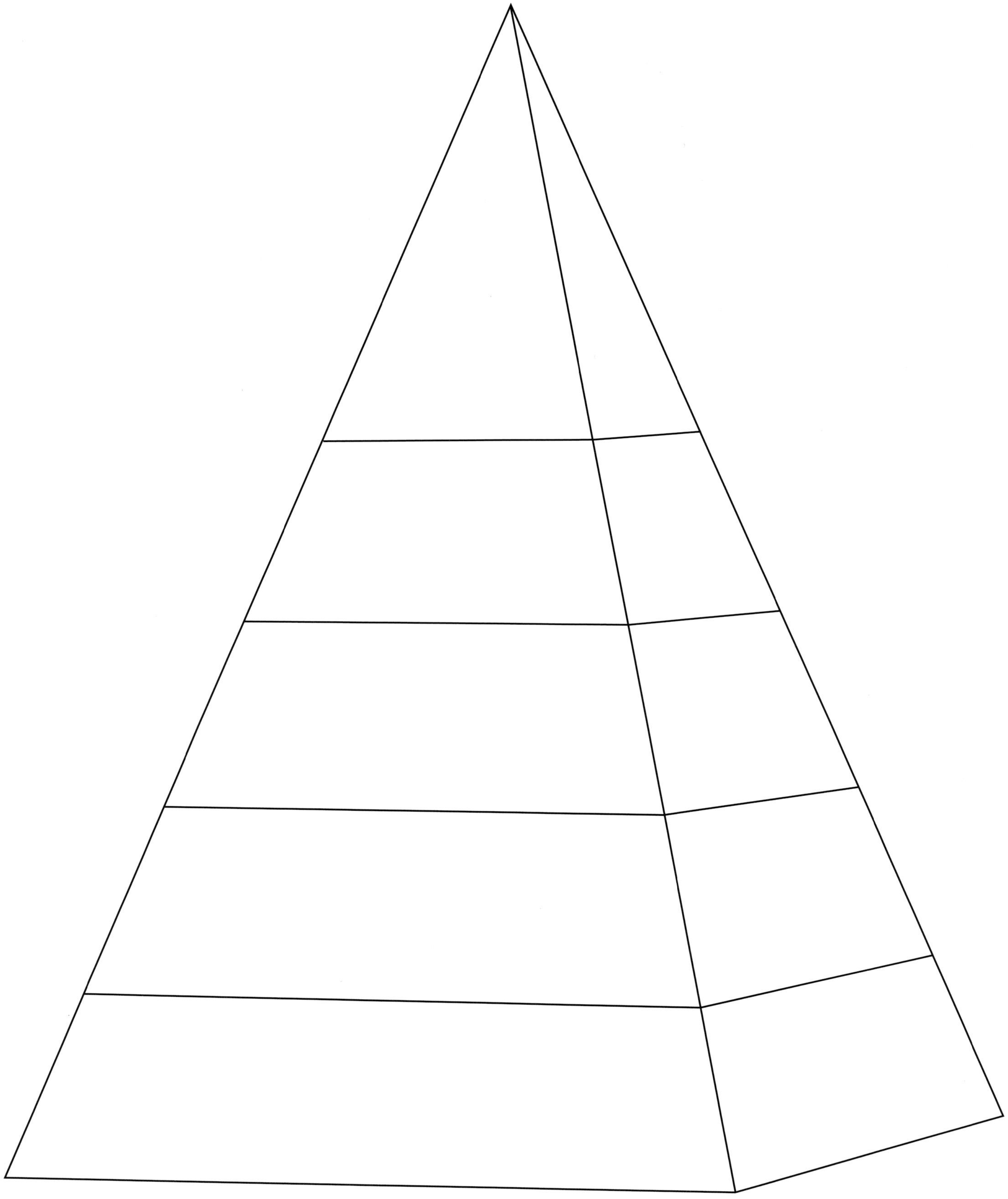

Name: ______________________________

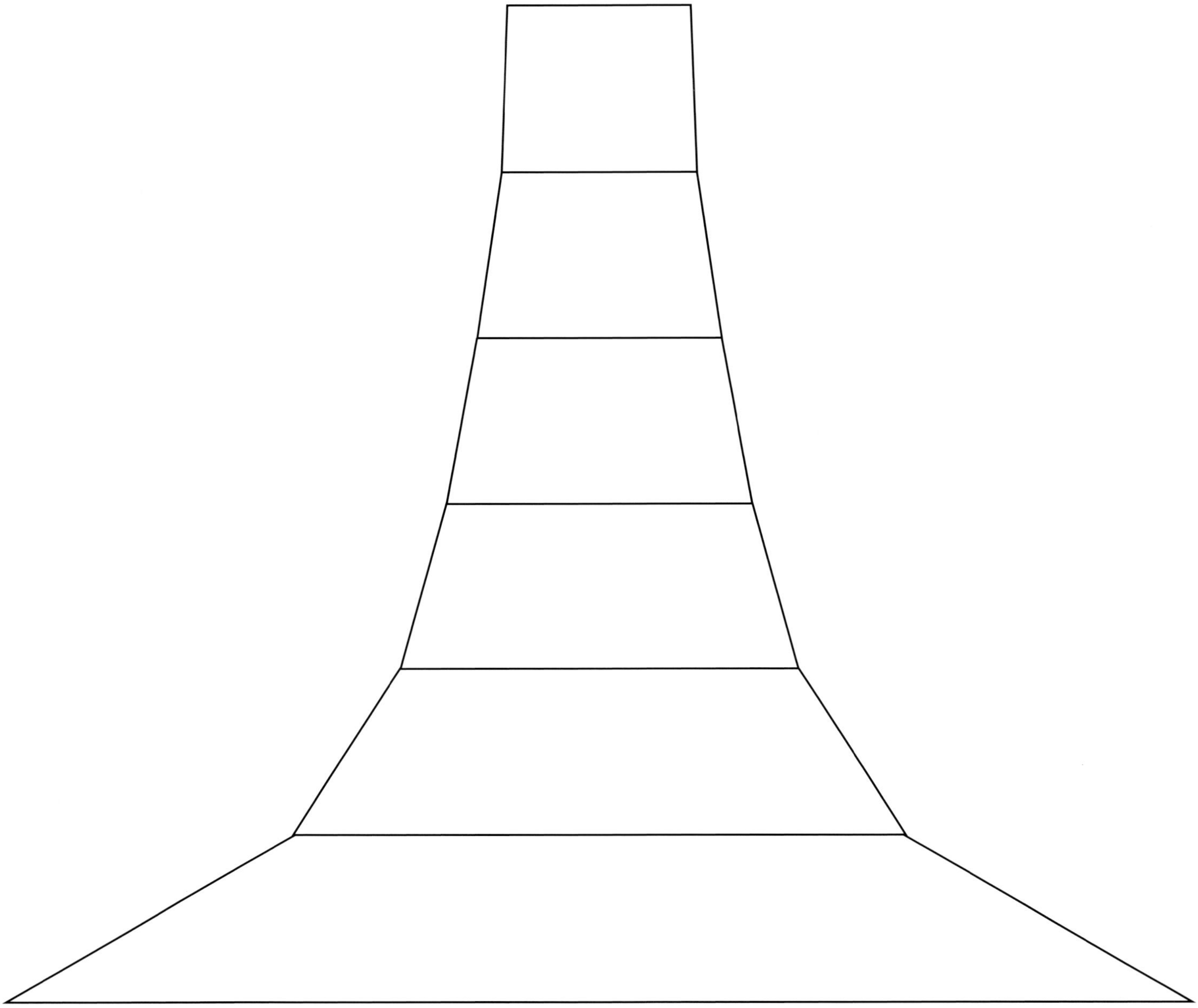

Name: ____________________

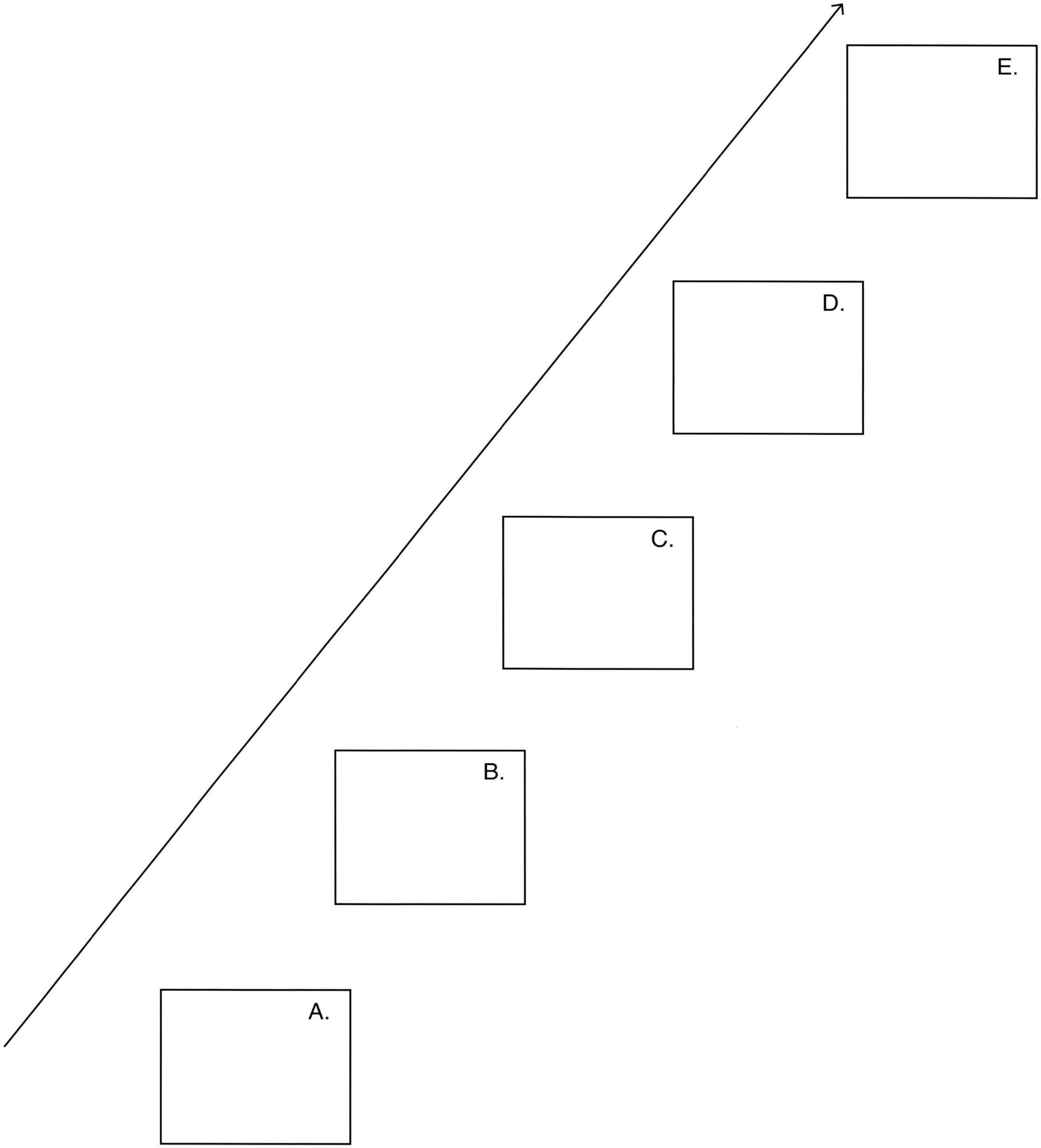

Name: ______________________________

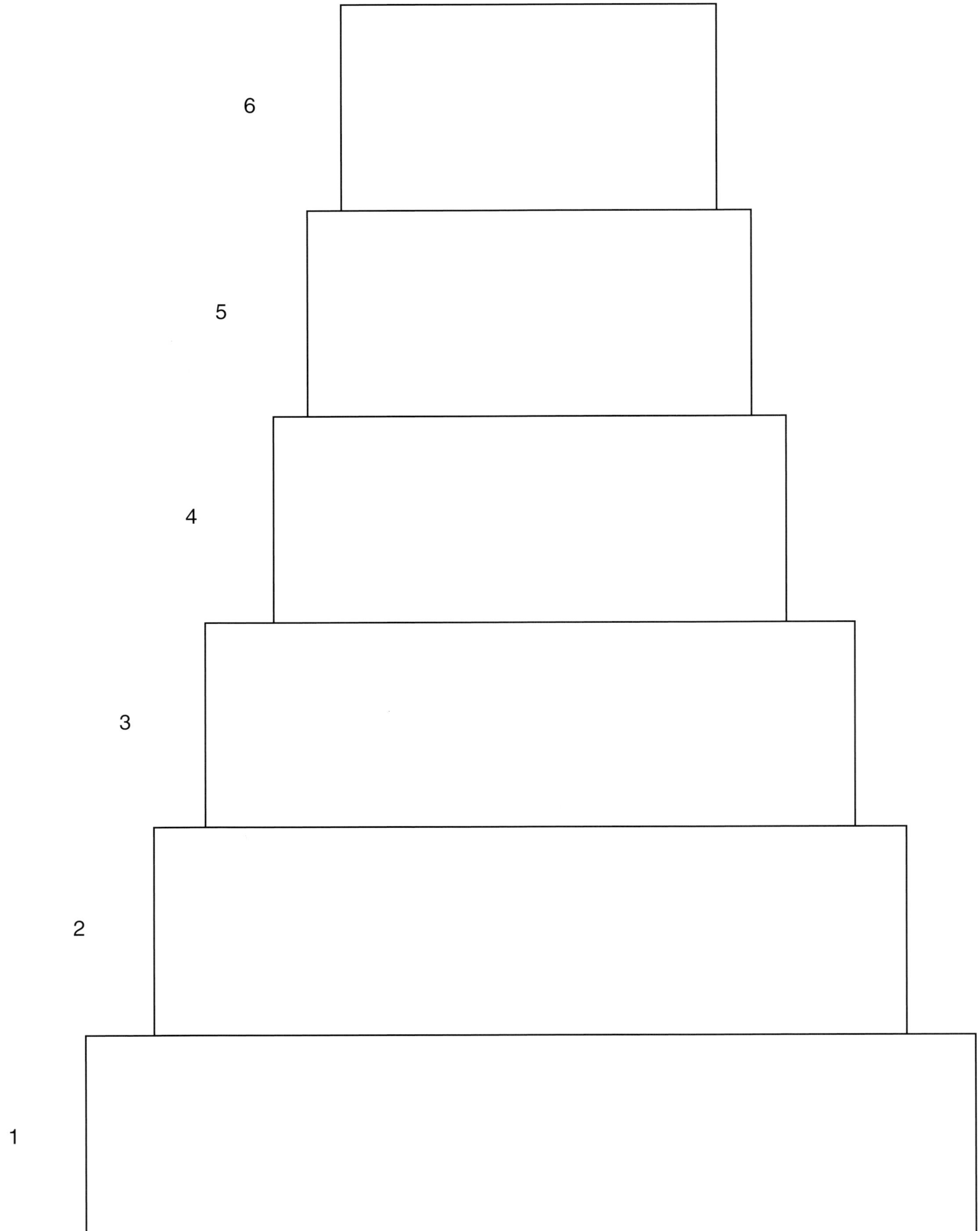

Name: ____________________

Name: ______________________________

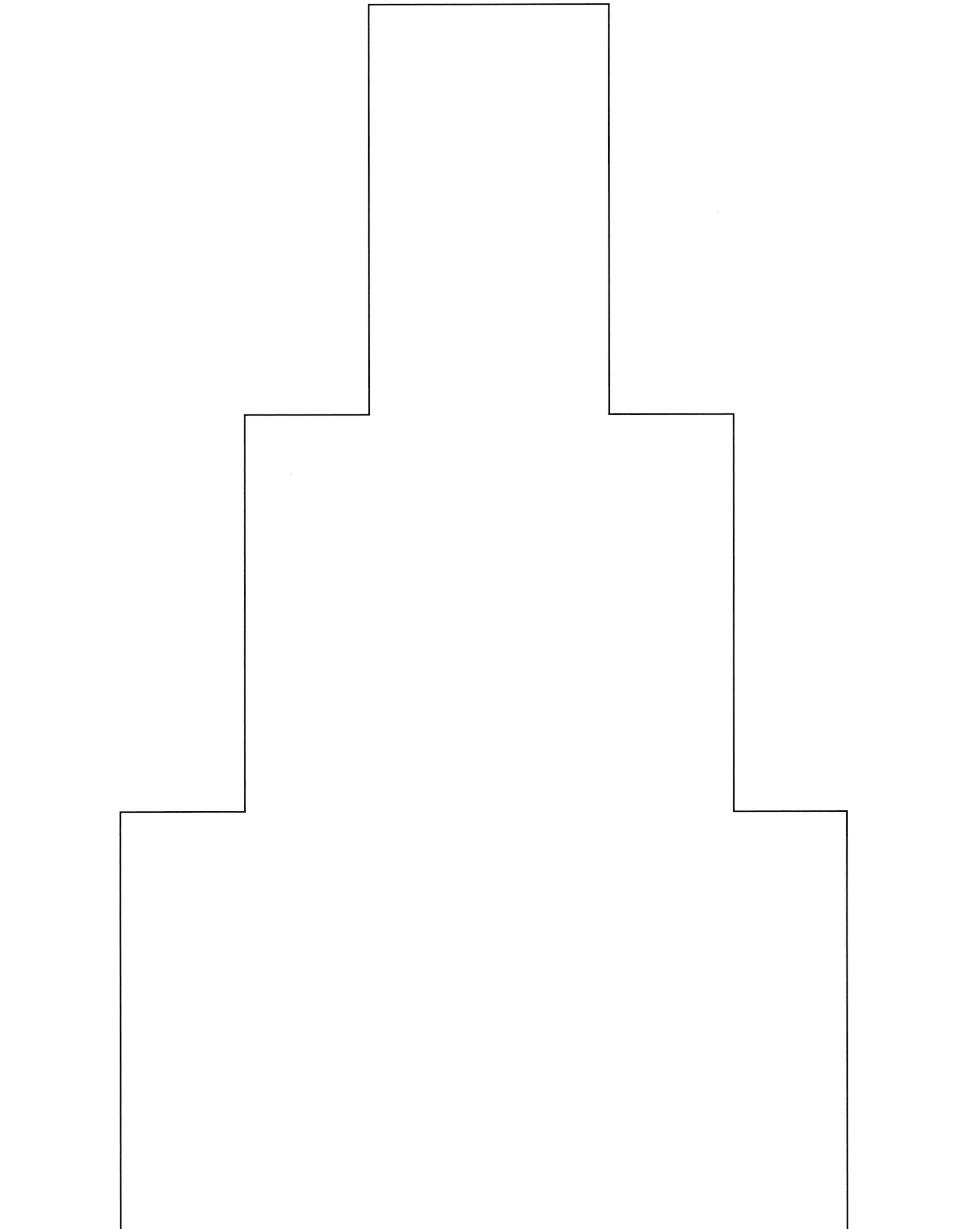

Name: ______________________

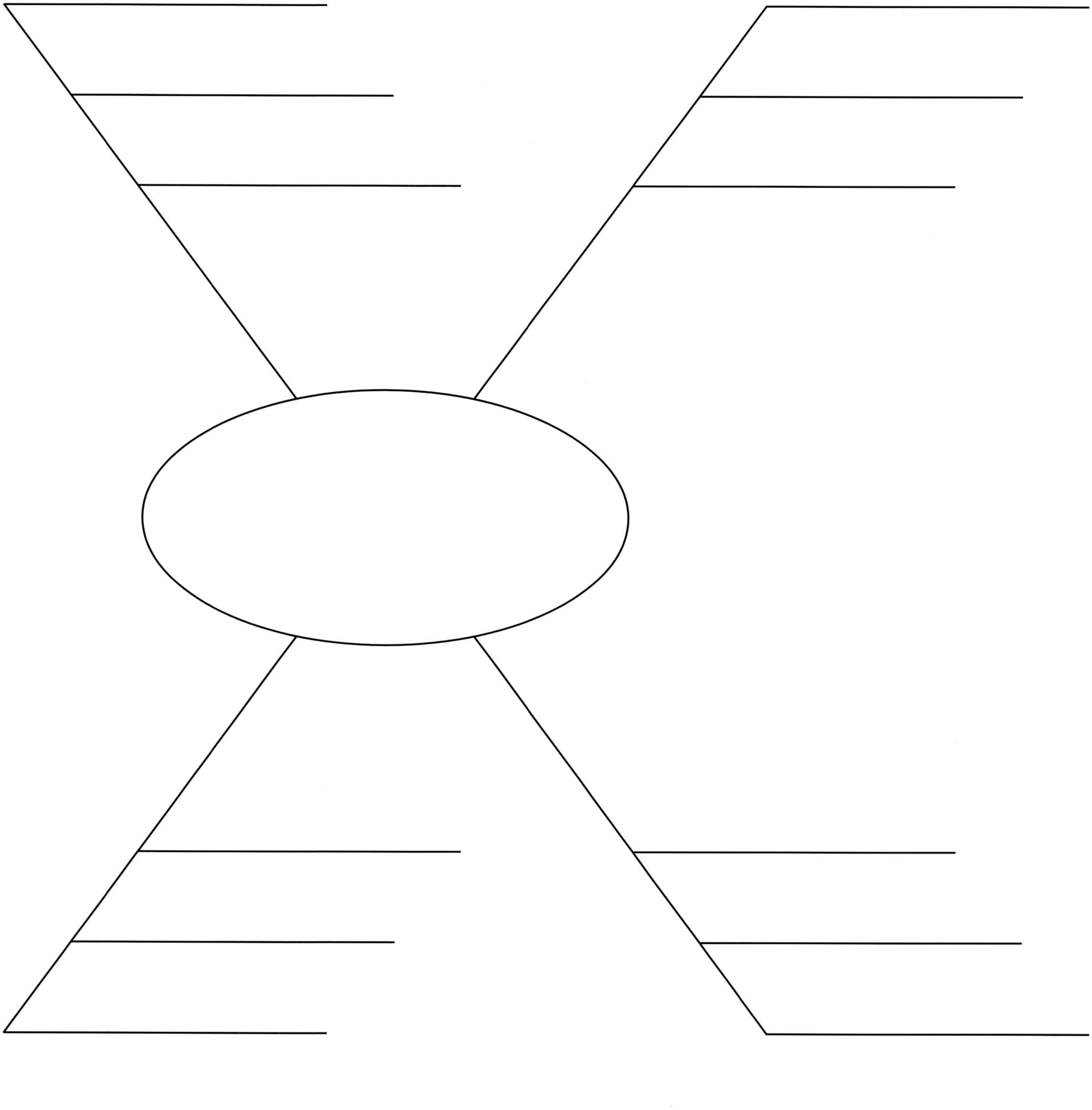

Name: ______________________________

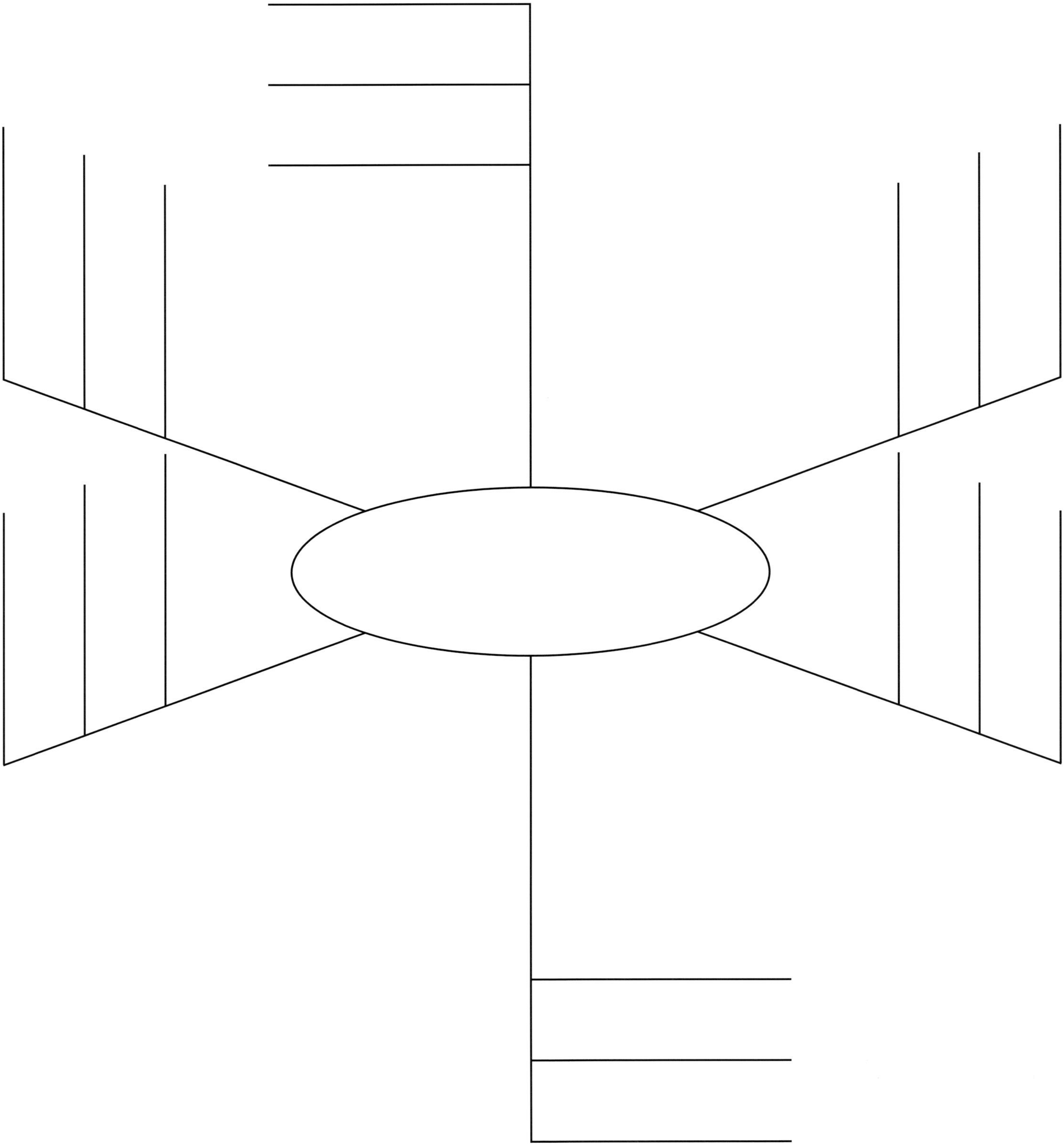

Name: ______________________________

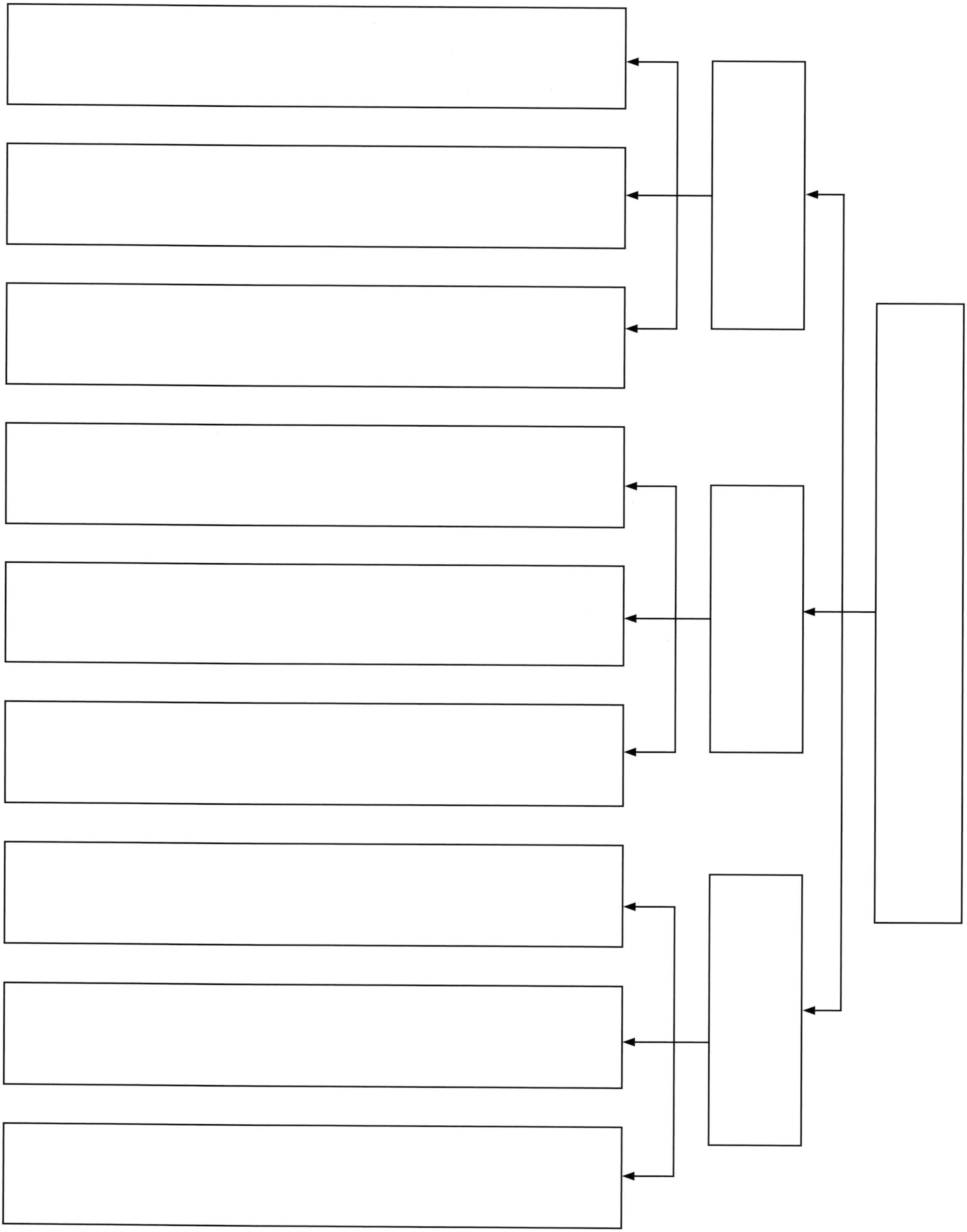

Name: ______________________________

Name: ______________________________

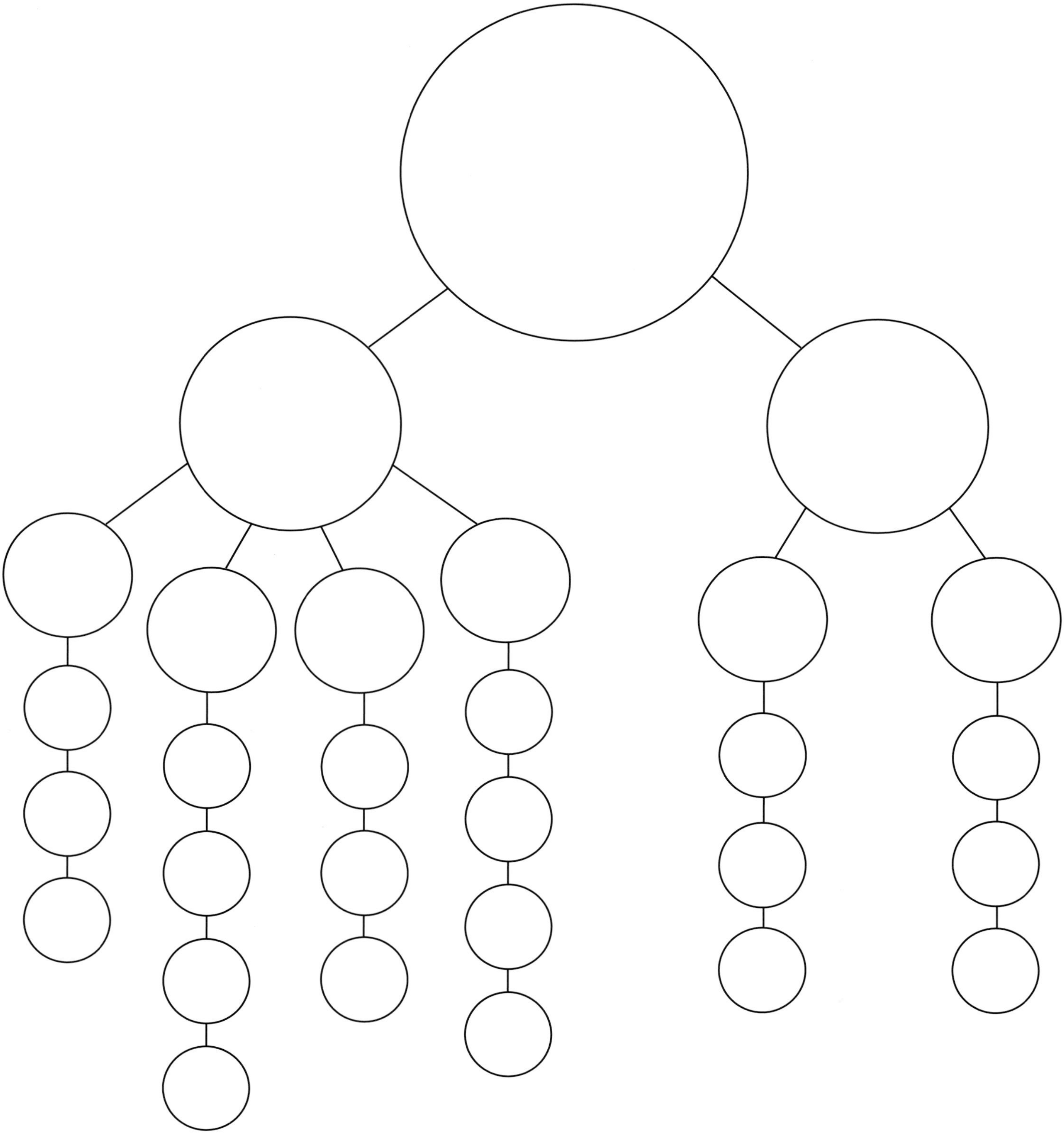

Name: ______________________________

Items

Name: ____________________

ITEM	OBSERVATION CATEGORY			
	A	B	C	D
1.				
2.				
3.				
4.				
5.				
6.				
7.				
8.				
9.				
10.				

Name: ______________________

CATEGORY 1	CATEGORY 2	CATEGORY 3	CATEGORY 4	CATEGORY 5

Name: ____________________

Name: ______________________________

Name: ____________________

Name: ____________________

Items to be compared

Properties	A.	B.	C.	
1.				Similarities Differences
2.				Similarities Differences
3.				Similarities Differences
4.				Similarities Differences
5.				Similarities Differences
6.				Similarities Differences
Conclusions				

Name: ____________________

Name: ____________________

A: ____________ B: ____________ C: ____________

True of A Only	True of A and B	True of B Only	True of B and C	True of C Only

Name: ______________________________

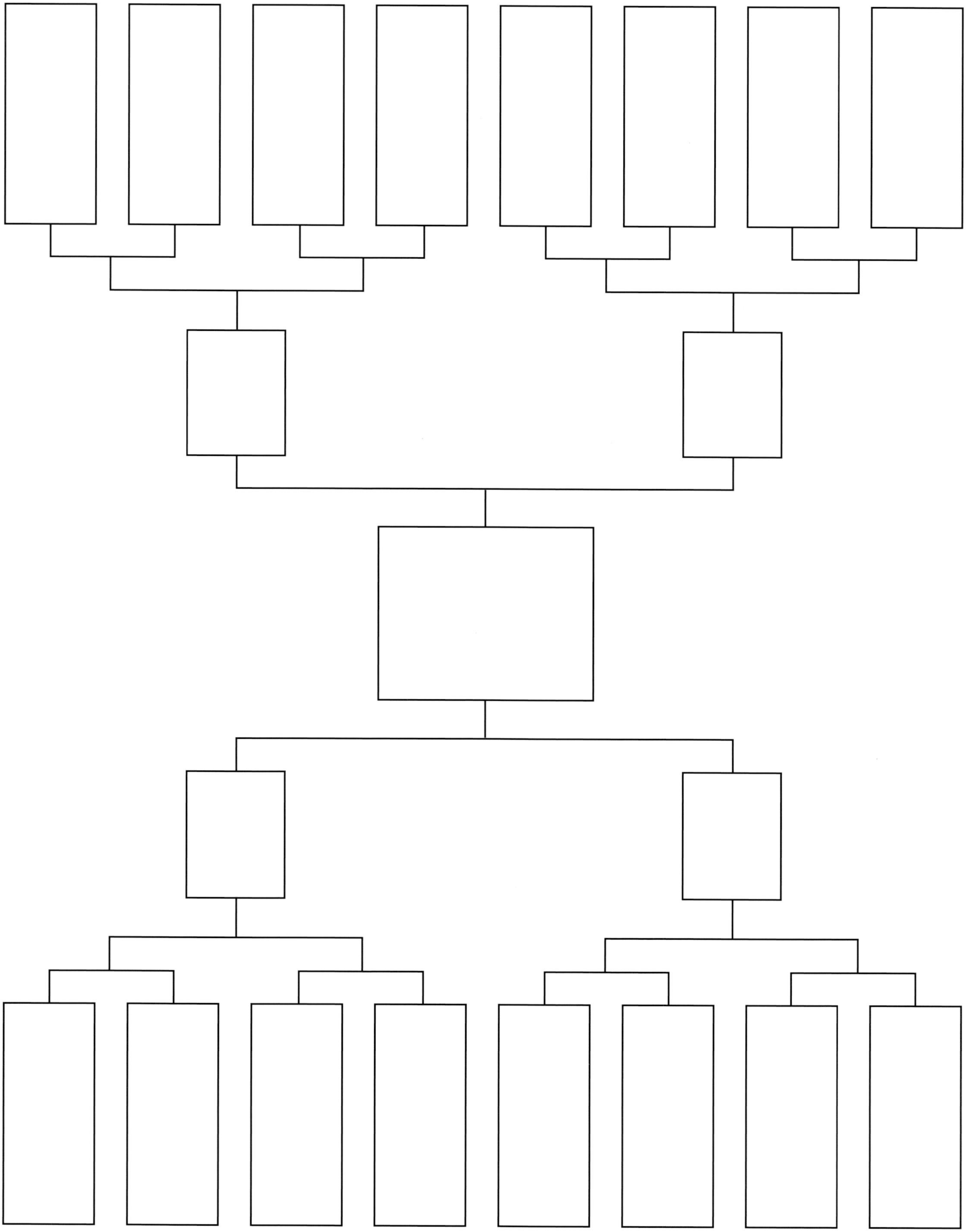

Name: ____________________

Alike	Different

Name: ____________________

Item	Alike	Different

Name: ____________________

____________________ ____________________

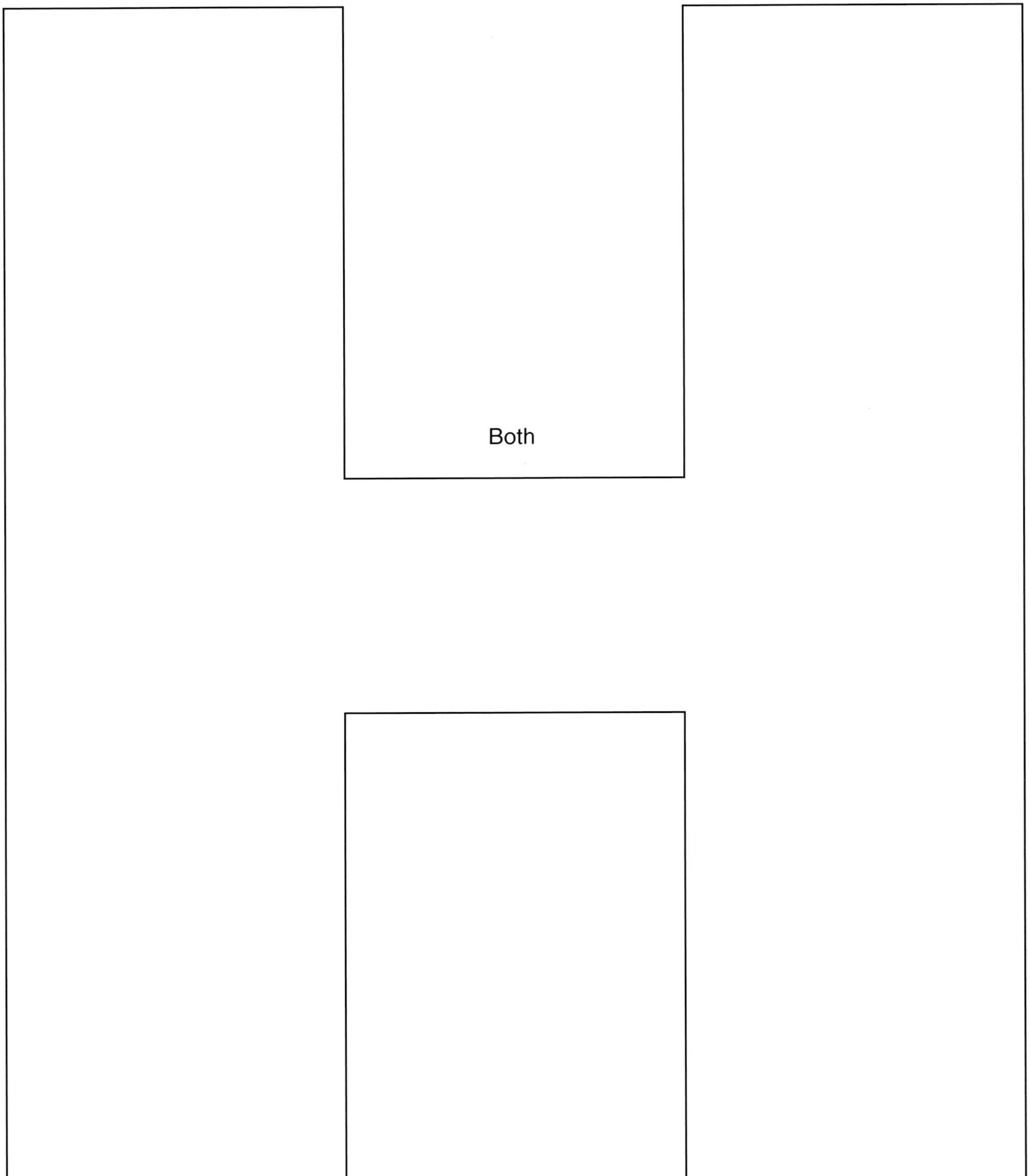

Name: ____________________

____________________ ____________________

Differences

Differences

Similarities

Differences

Differences

Name: ______________________

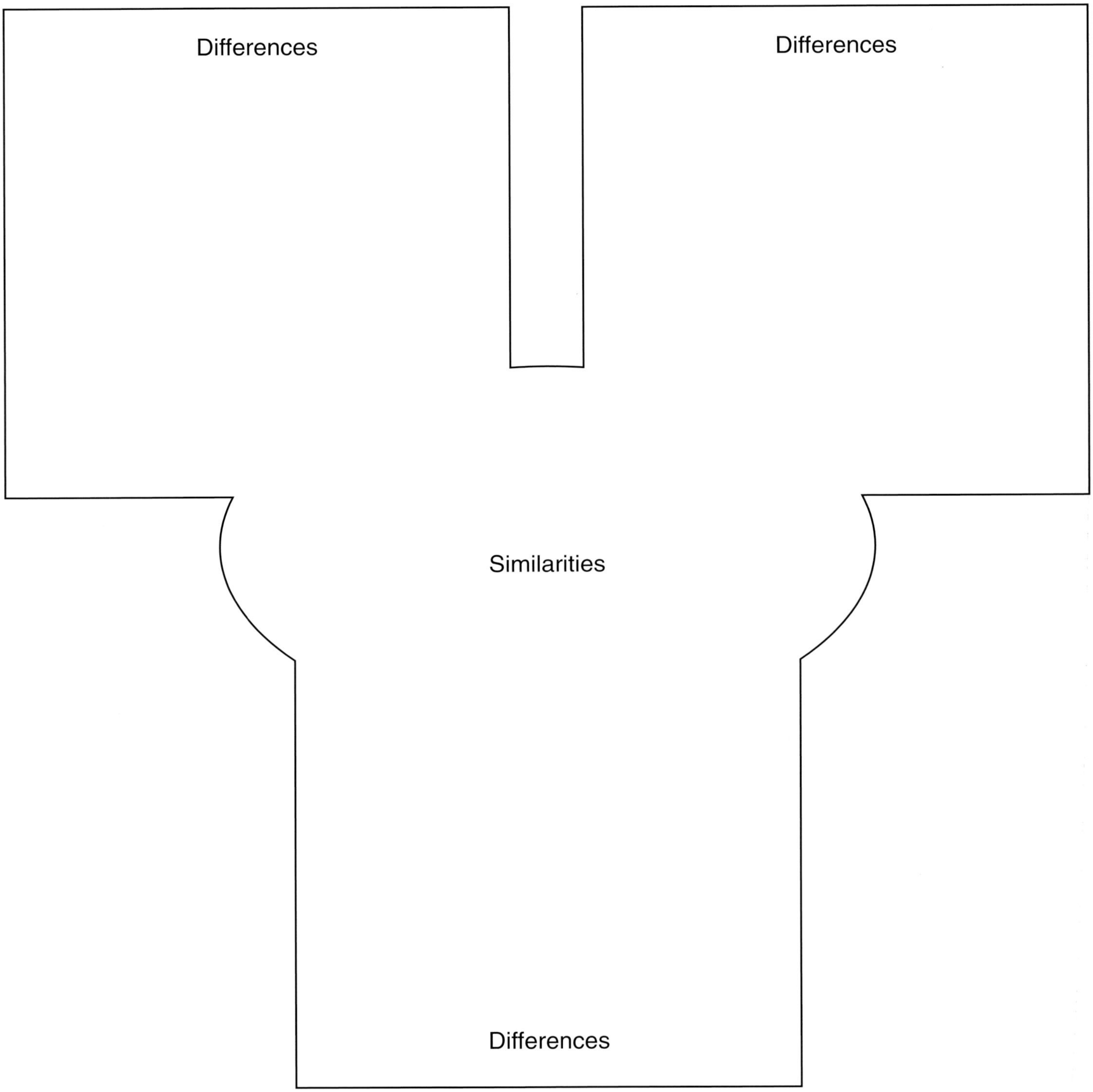

Name: ____________________

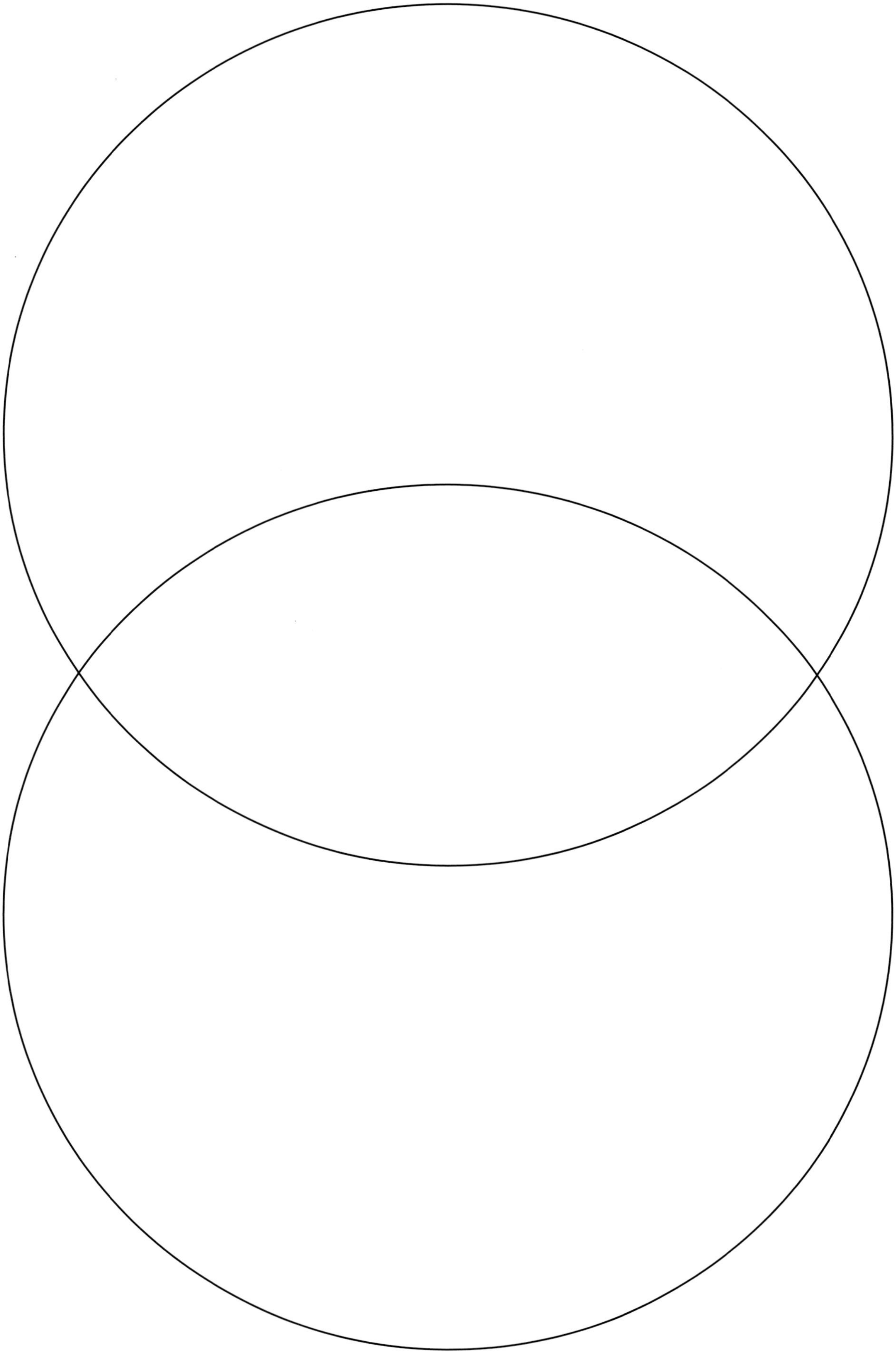

Name: ______________________________

Name: ______________________________

Comparing A ______________________________

B ______________________________

C ______________________________

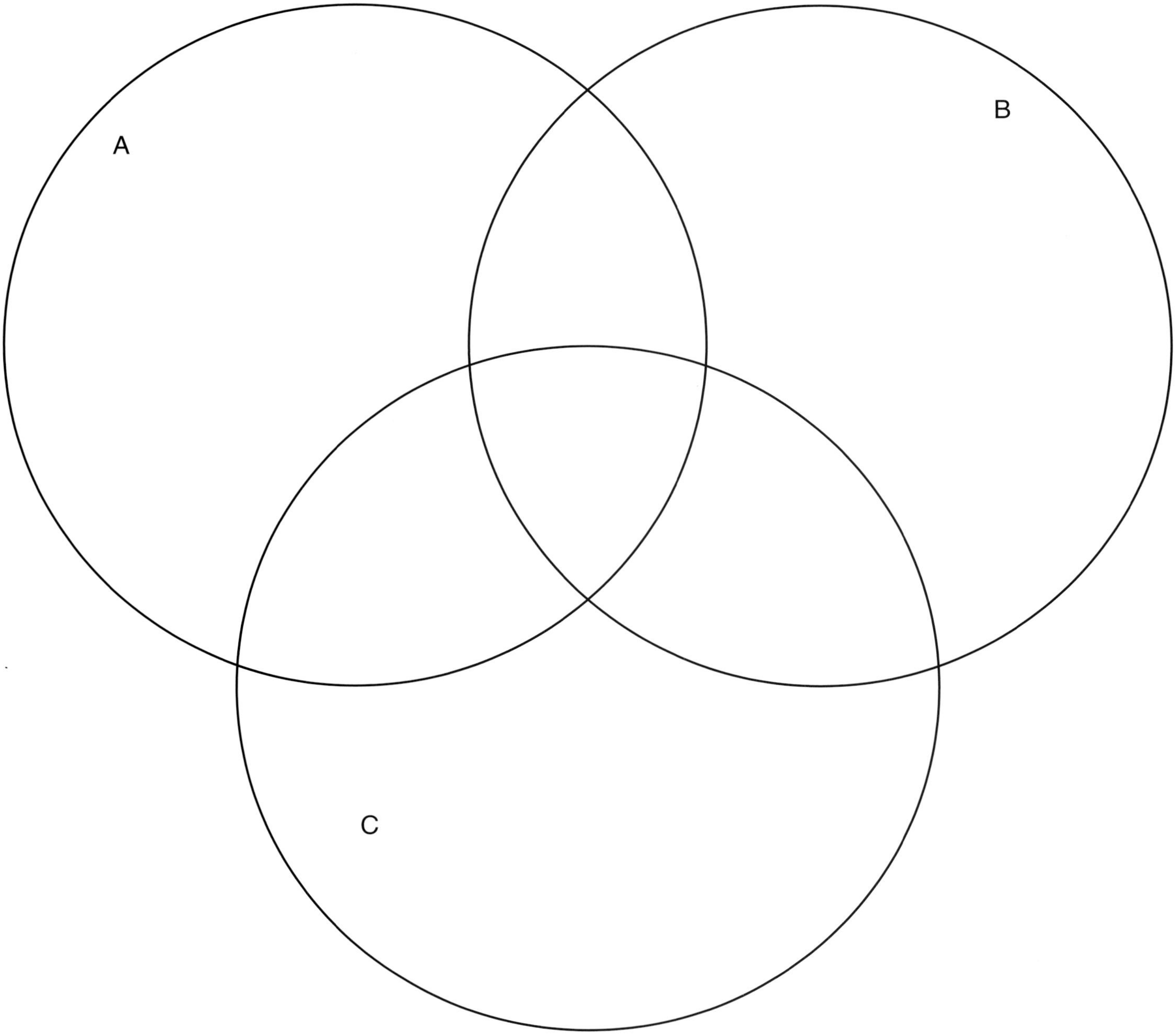

Name: ______________________________

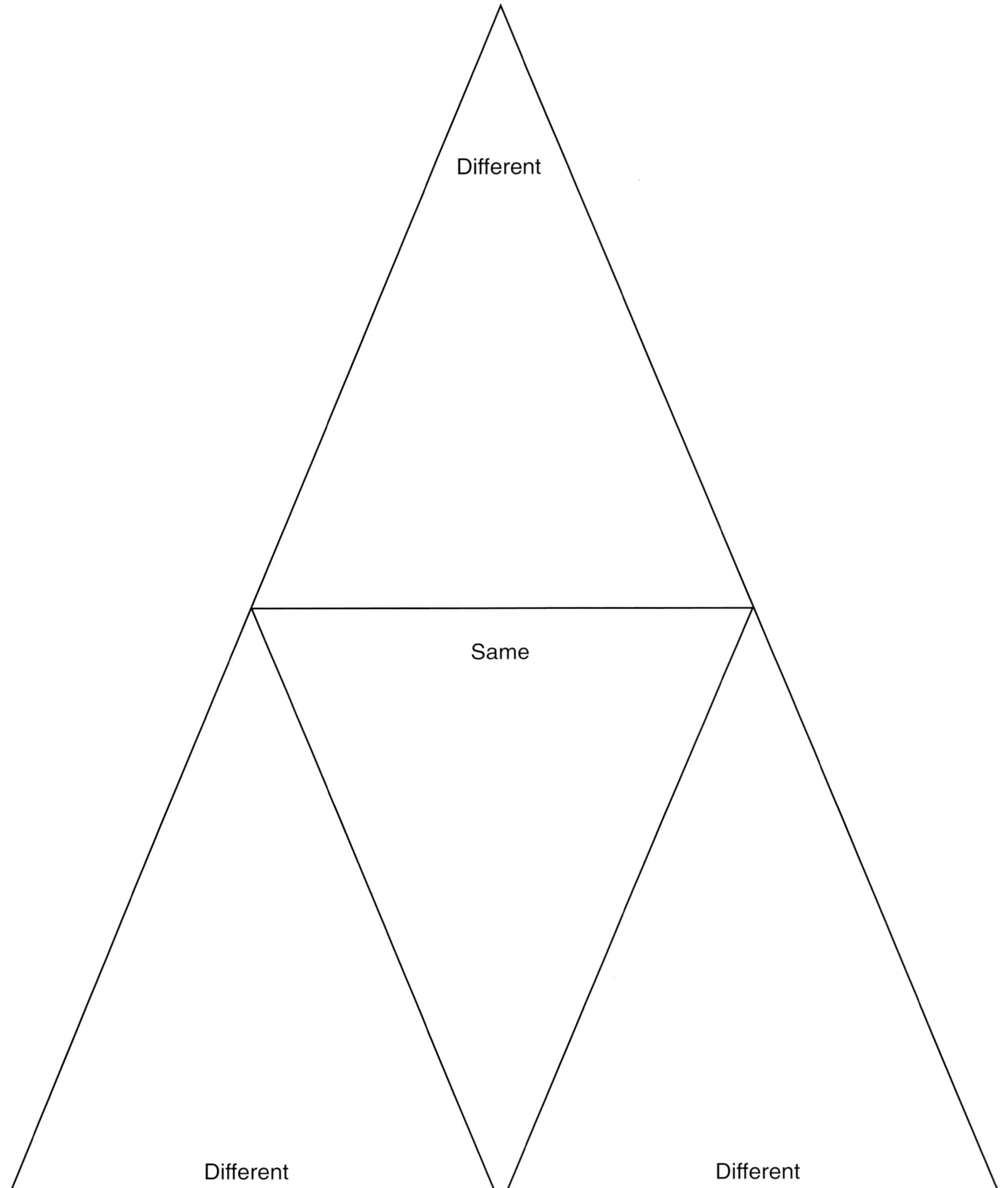

Name: ____________________

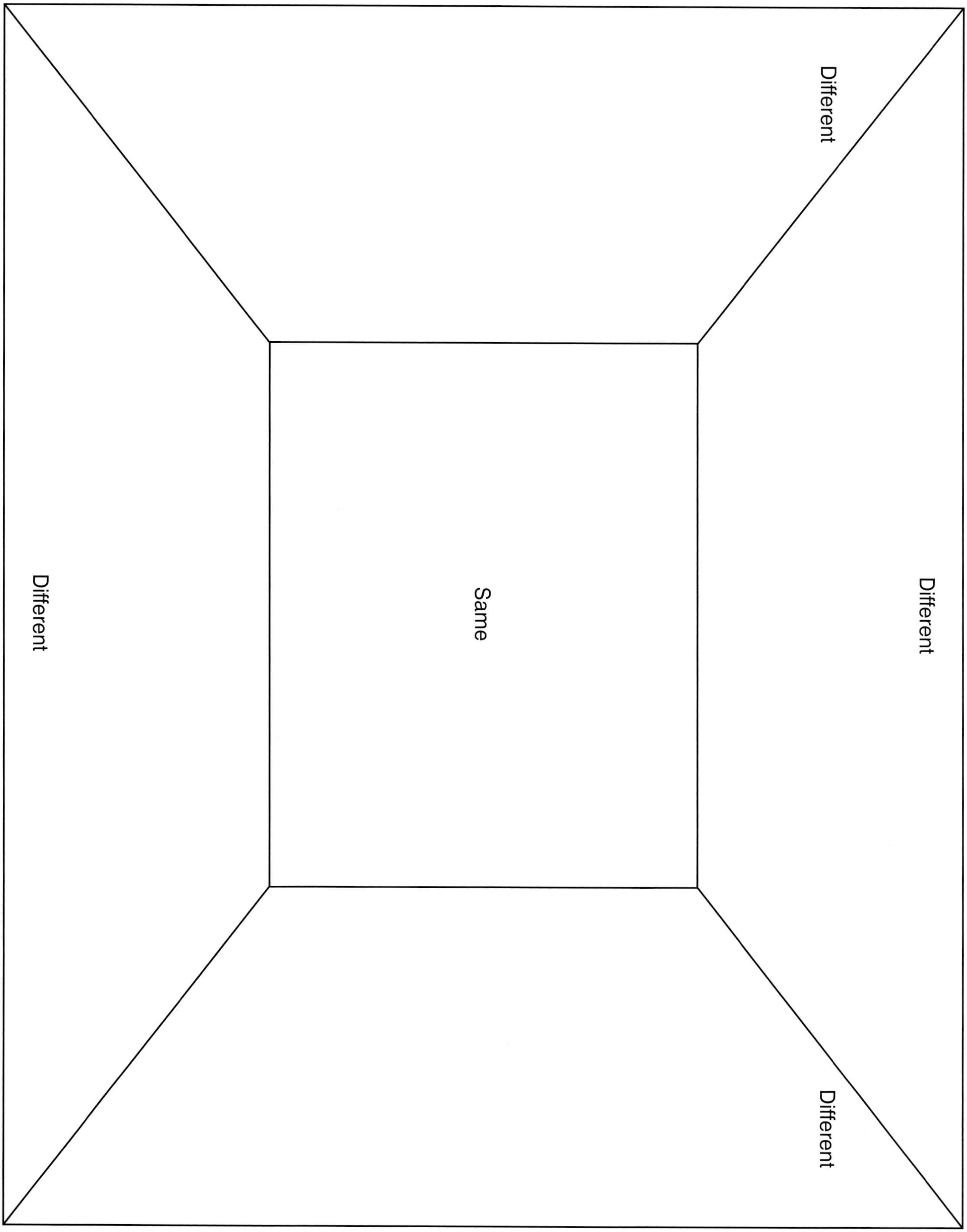

Name: ______________________________

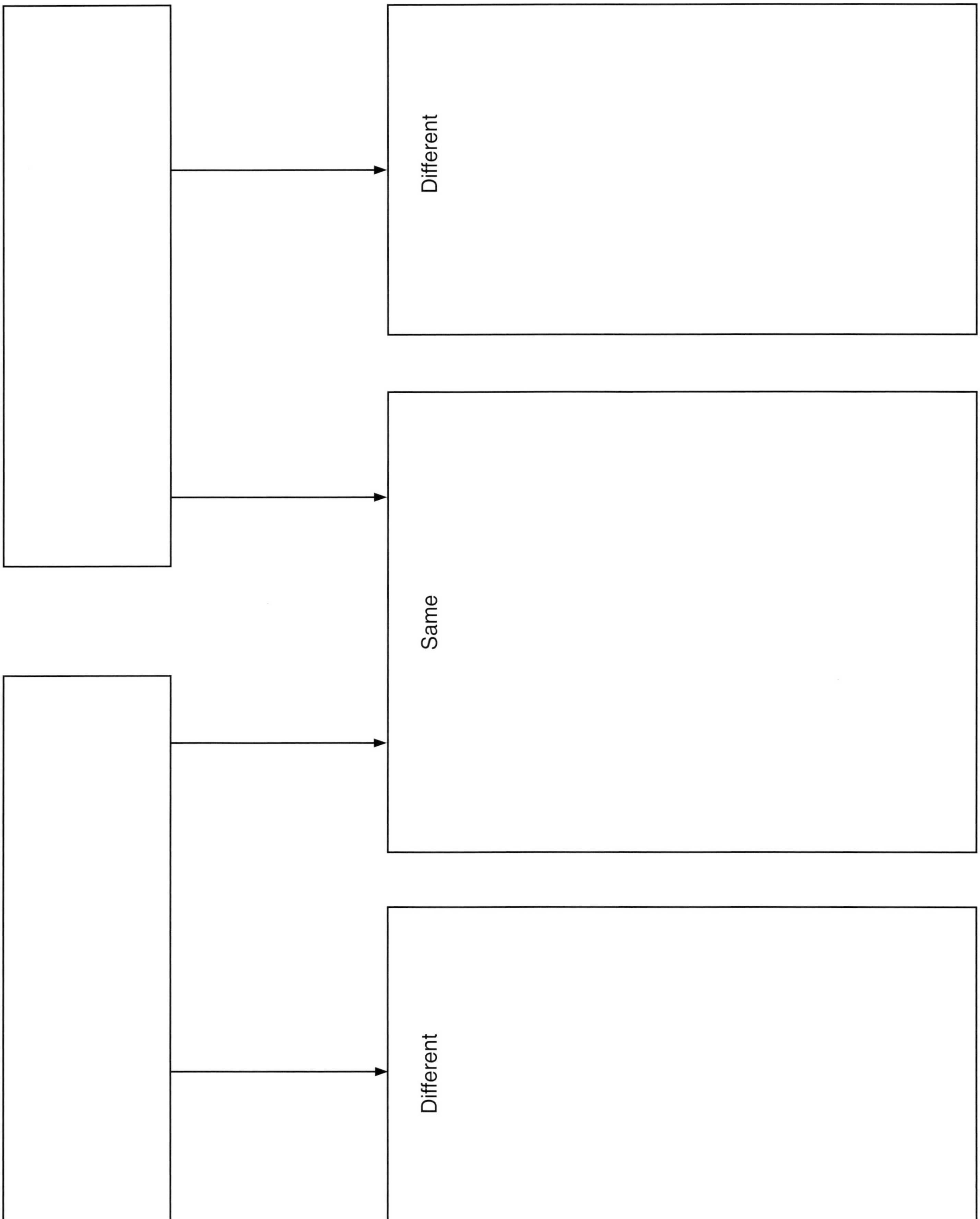

Name: ________________________________

____

How Alike?

How Different?

Name: ______________________________

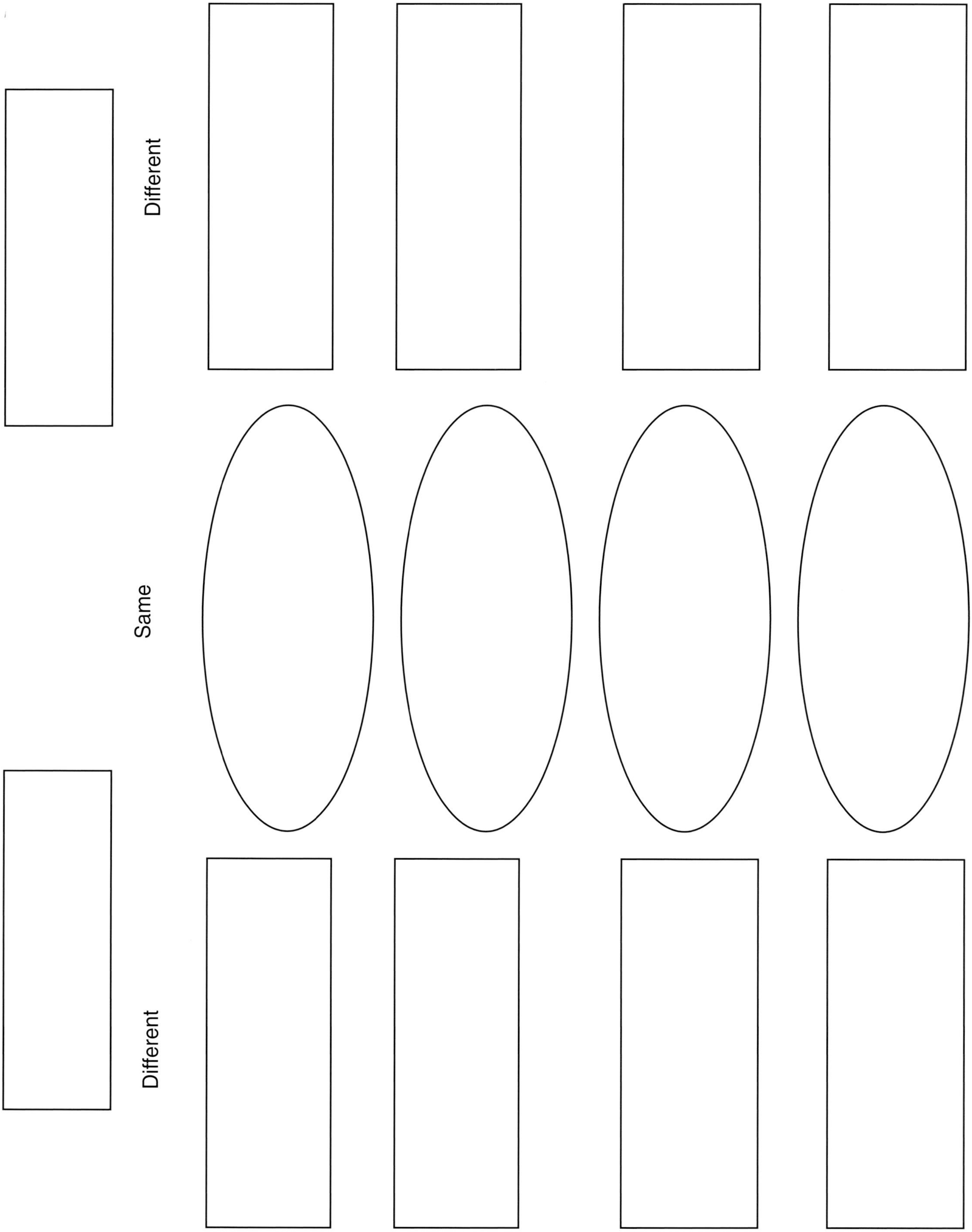

Name: ______________________

Concept 1 ______________________

Concept 2 ______________________

How Alike?

How Different?

With Regard To

Name: ______________________________

Name: ____________________

1. ____________________

2. ____________________

3. ____________________

Name: ______________________________

____

Name: ____________________

Cycle of

____

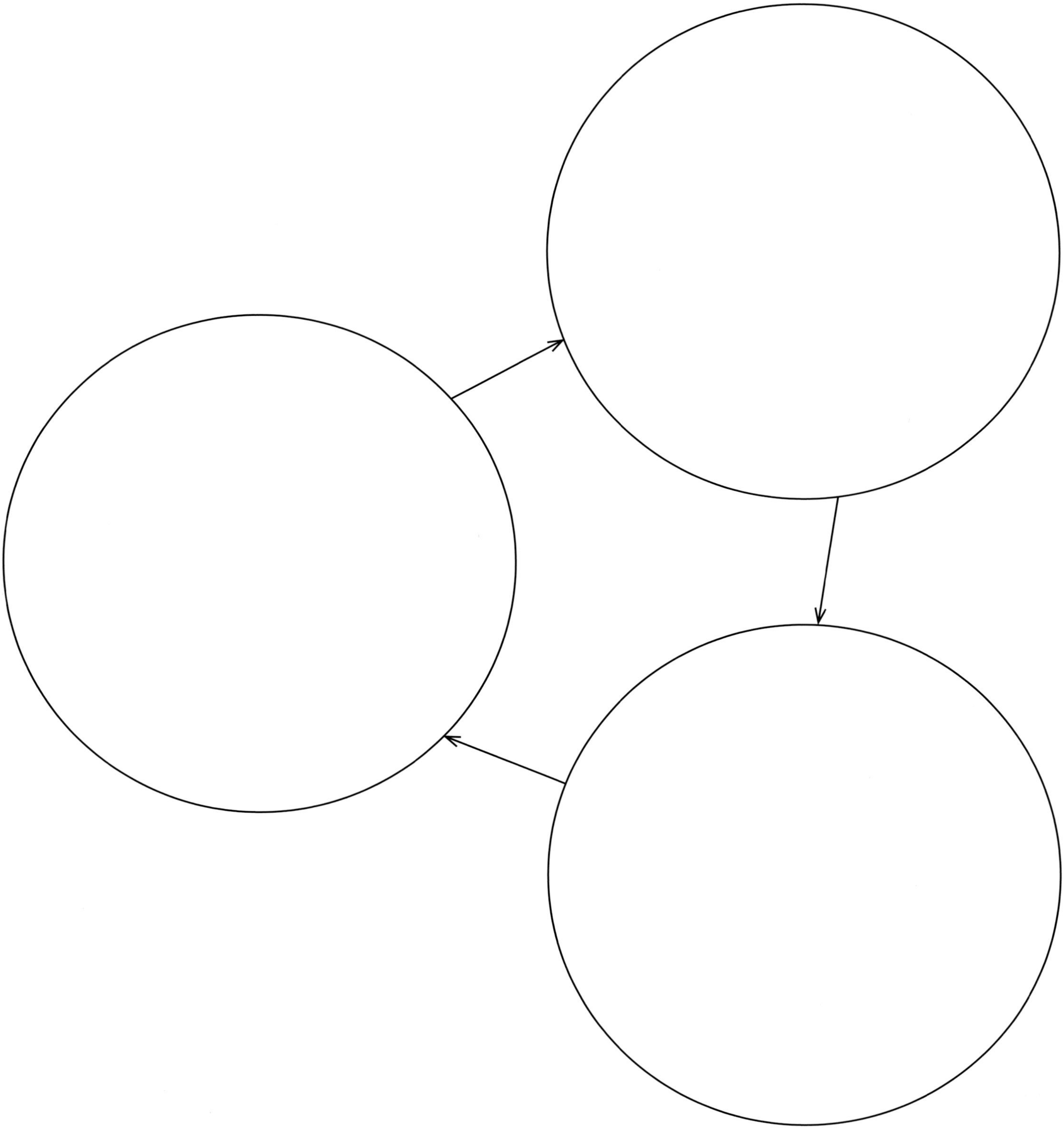

Name: ______________________________

Cycle of

____

Name: ______________________________

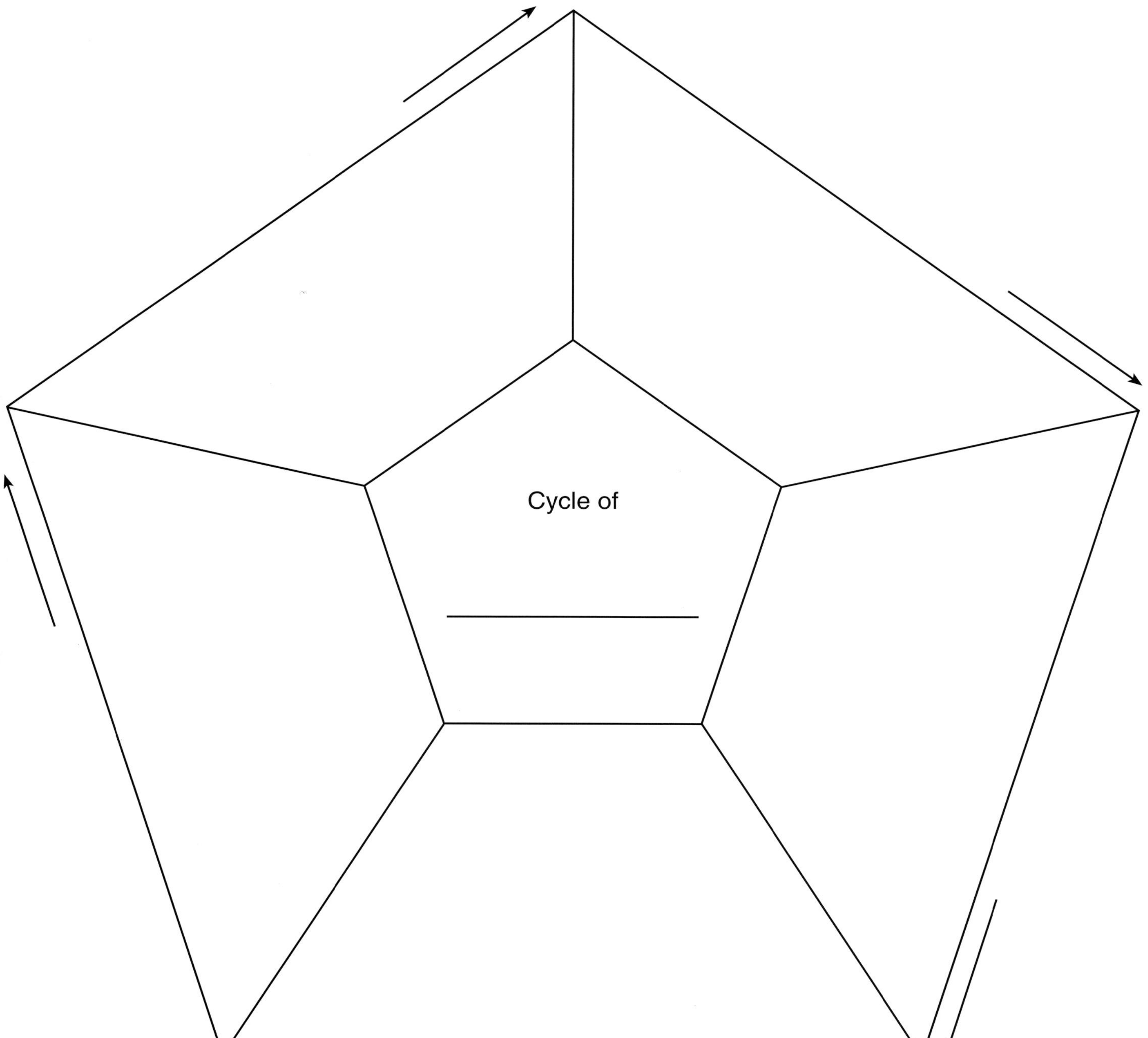

Name: ______________________

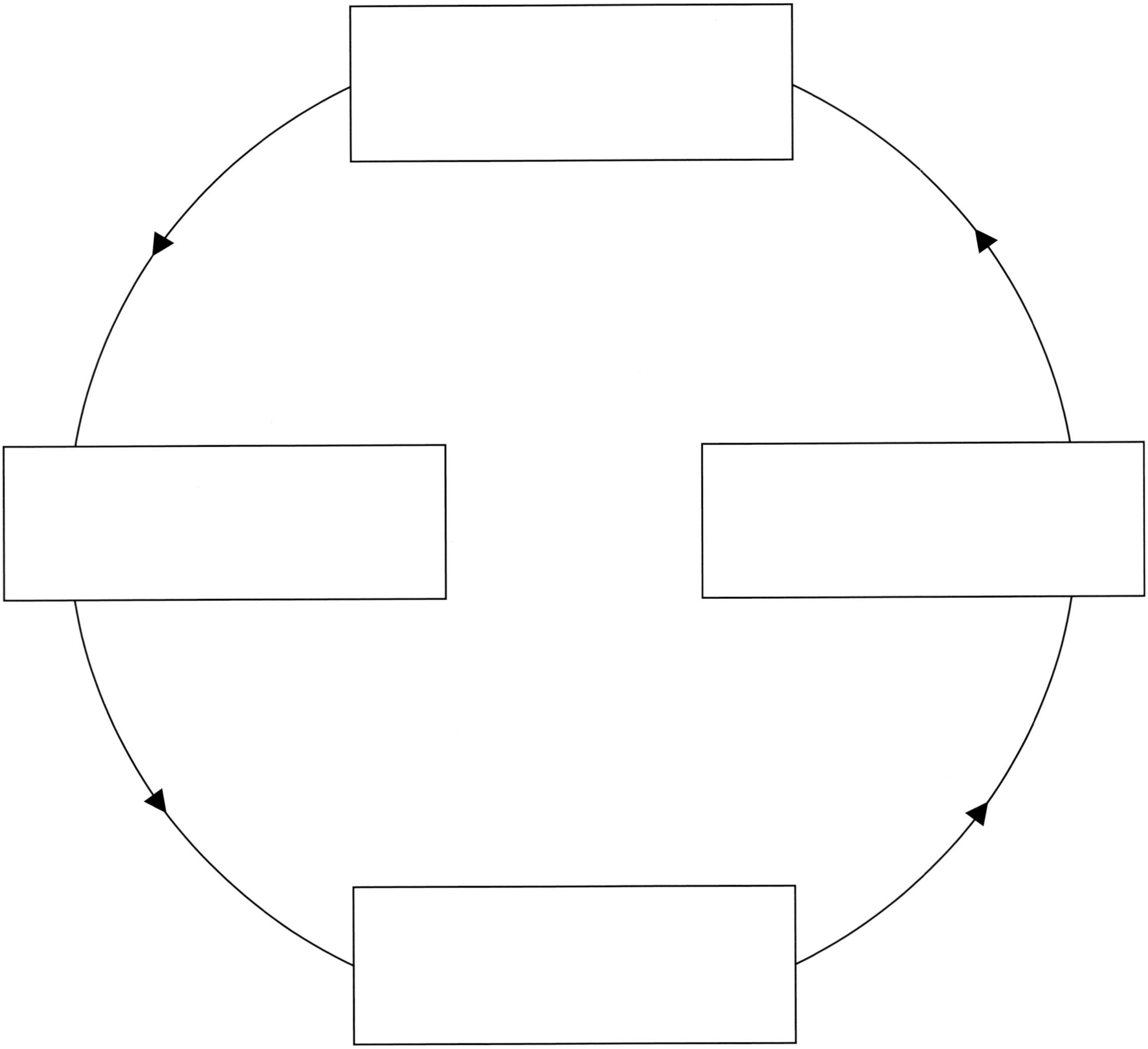

Name: ______________________________

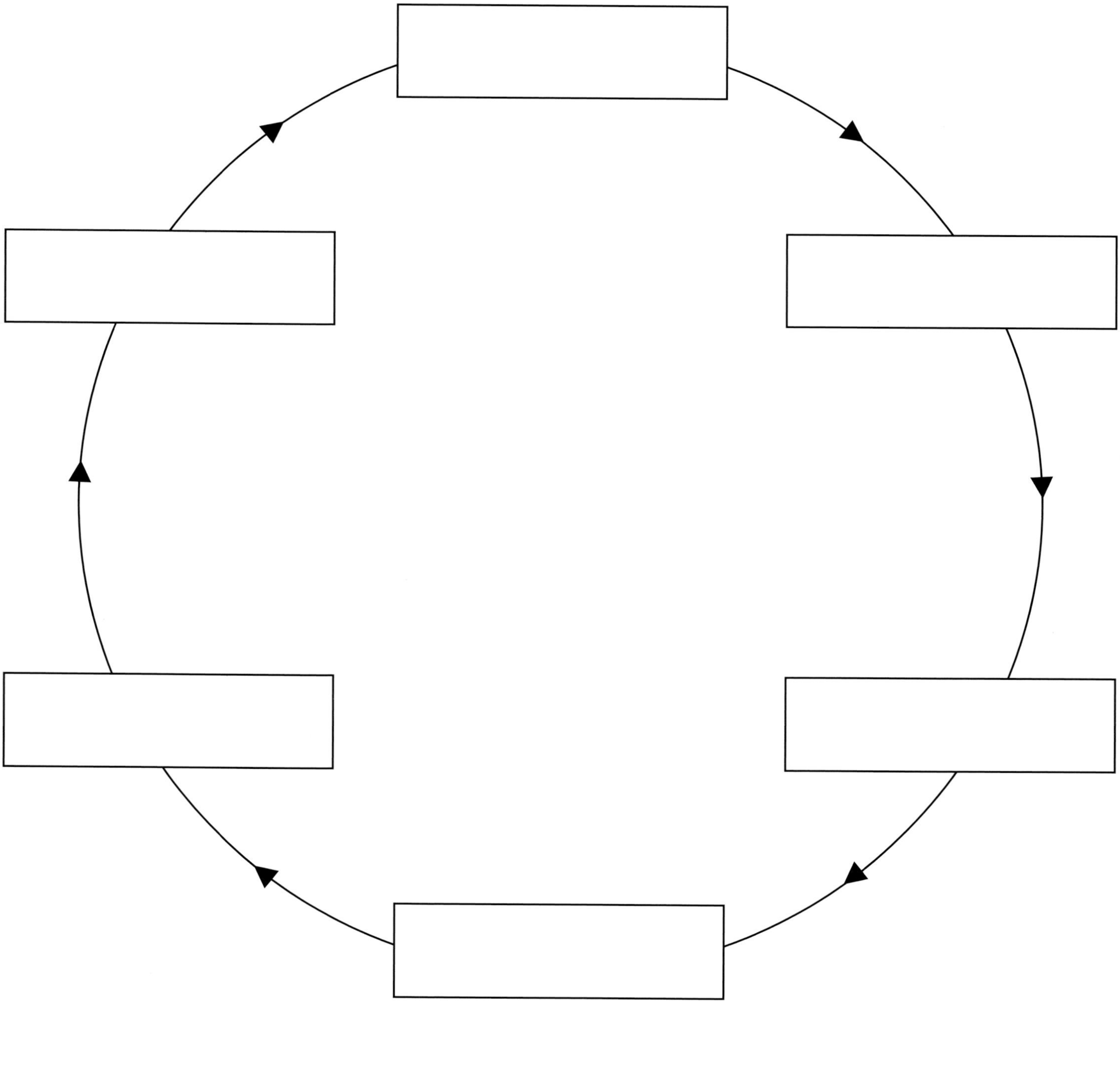

Name: ______________________________

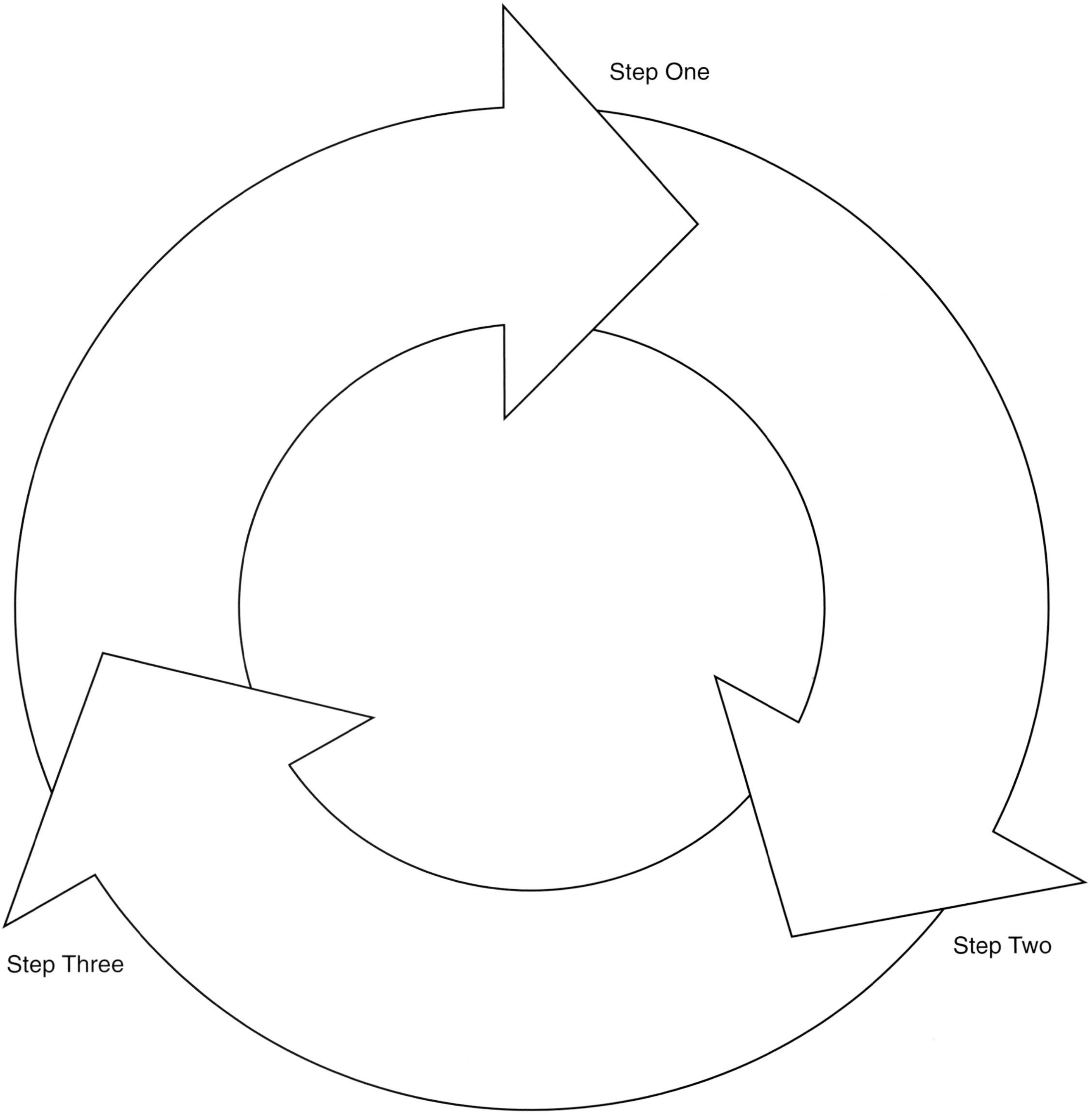

Name: ____________________________________

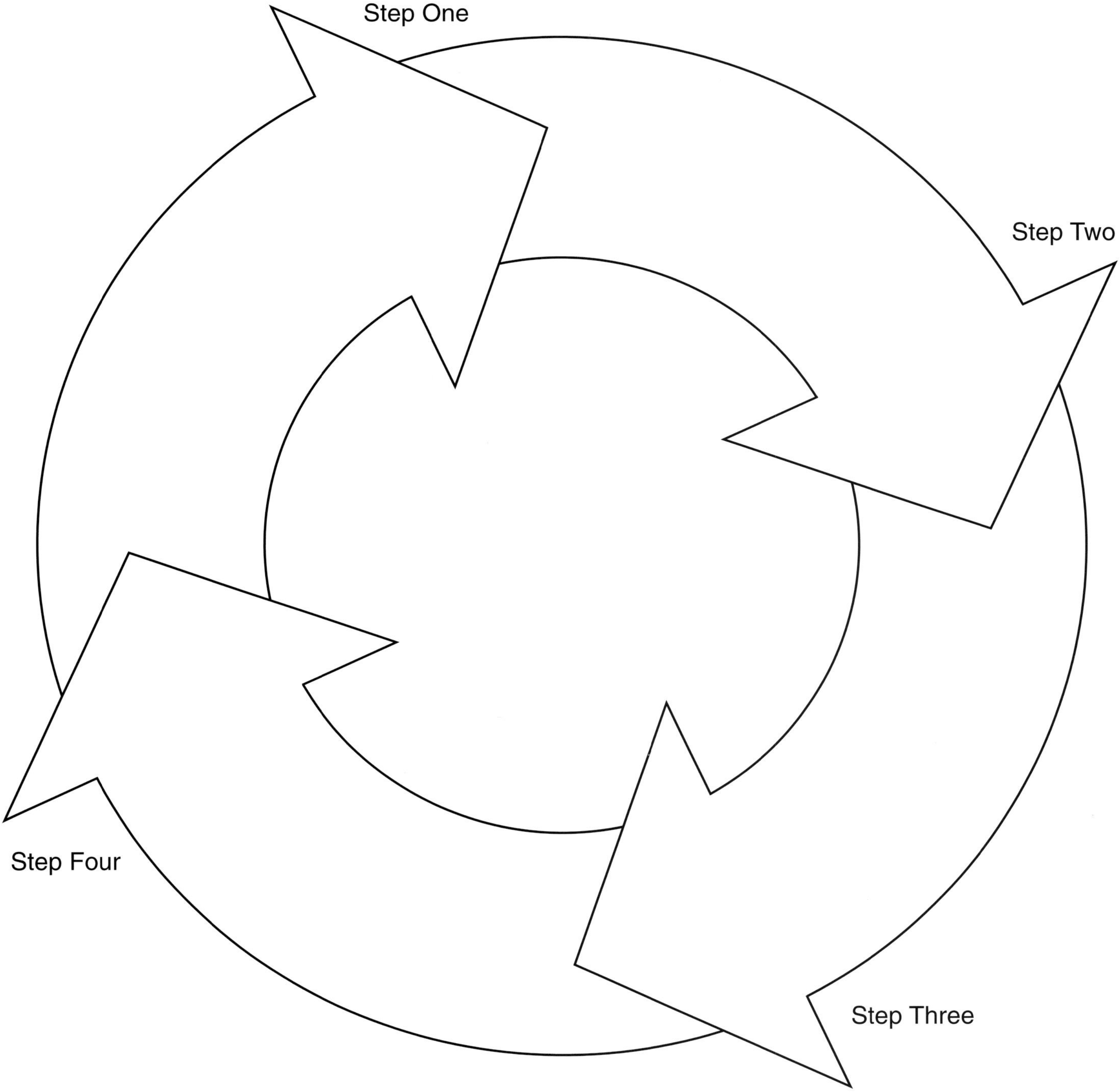

Name: ______________________________

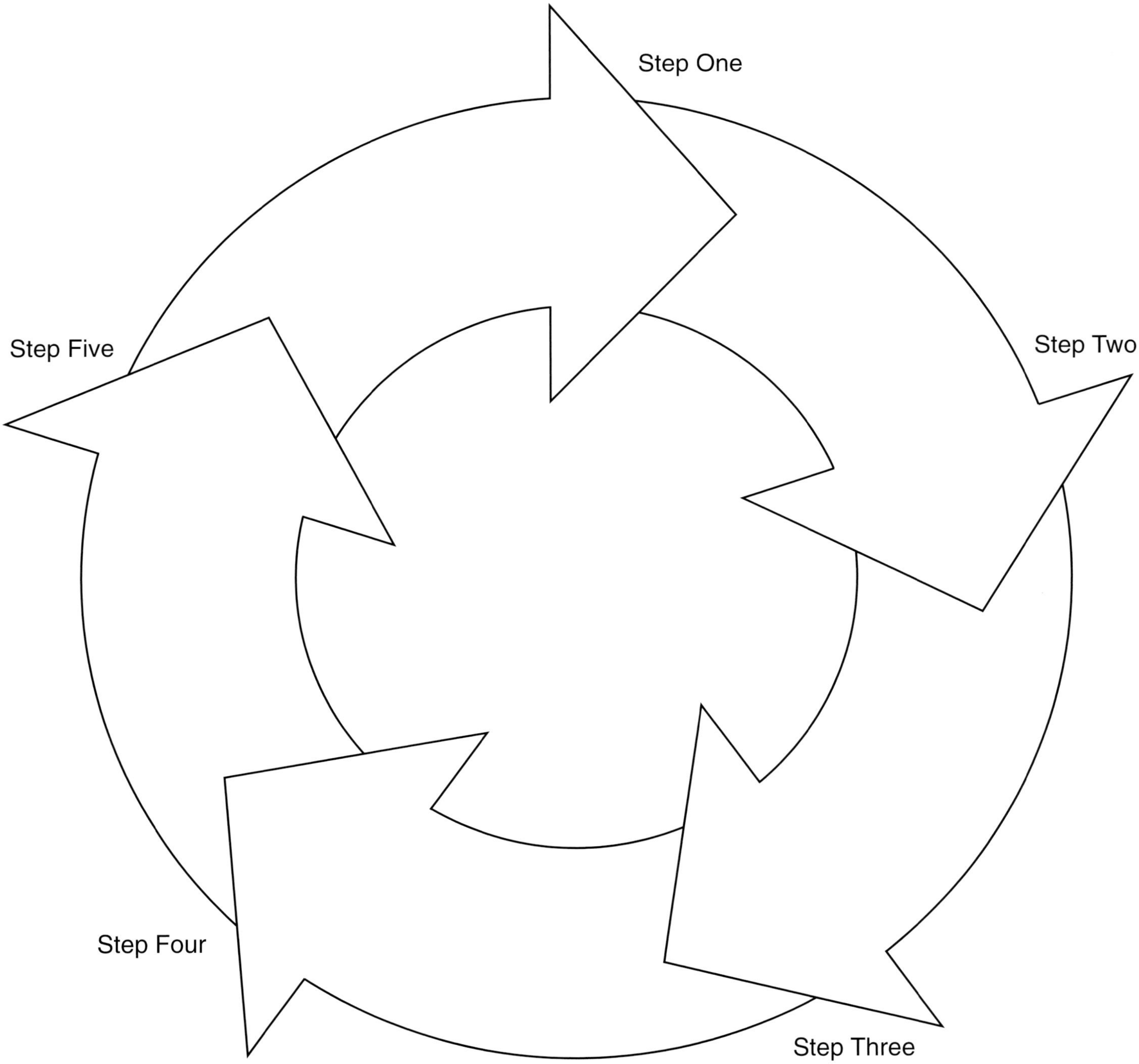

Name: ______________________________

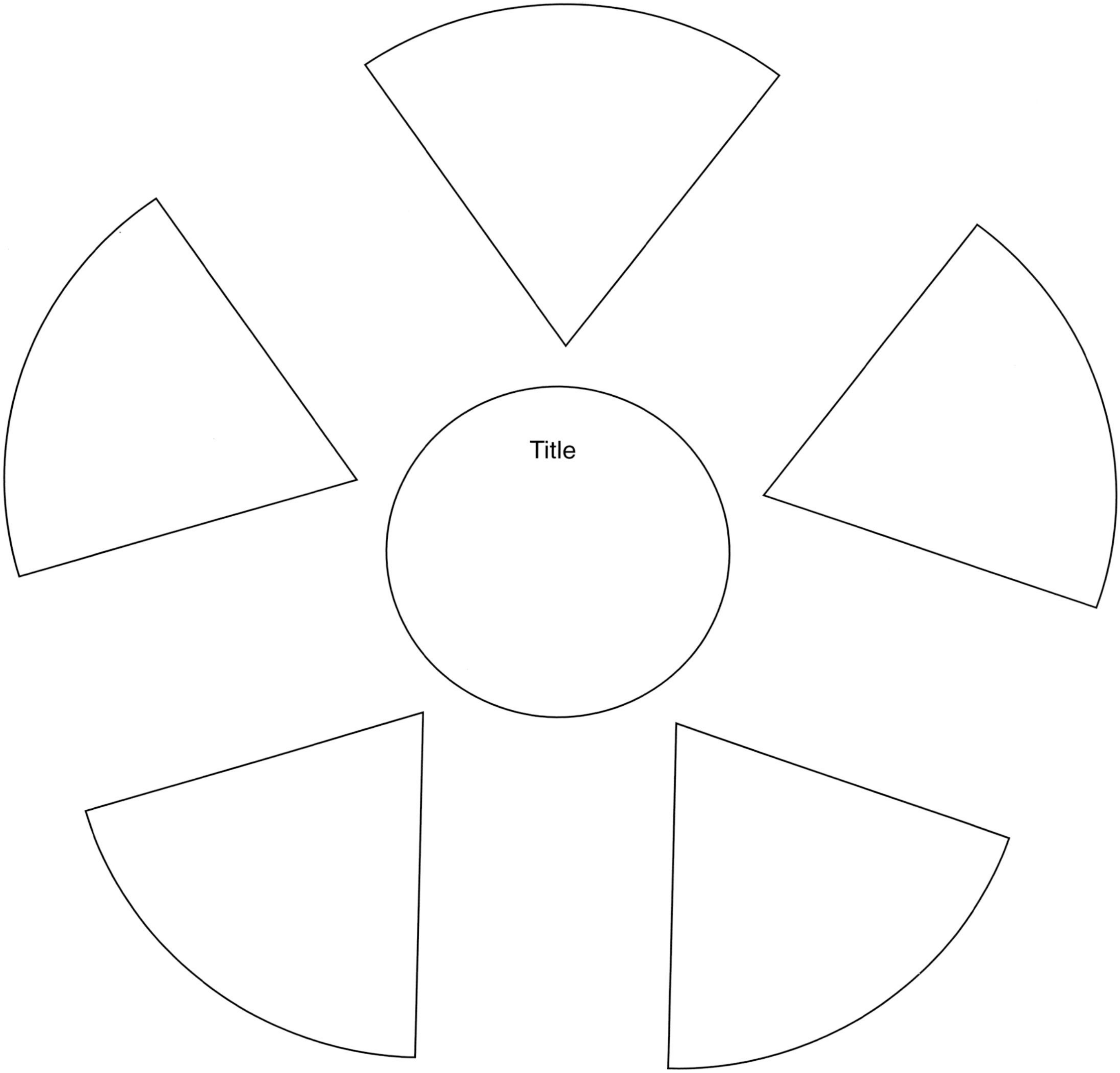

Name: ______________________________

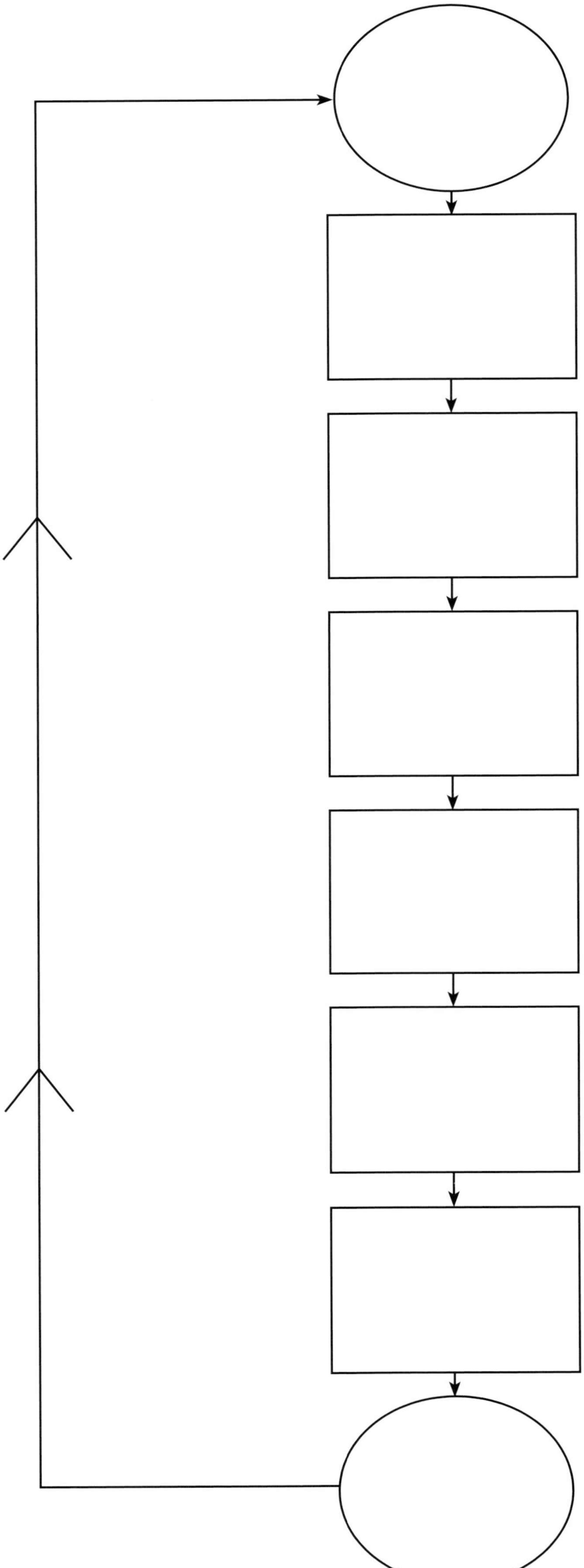

Name: ____________________

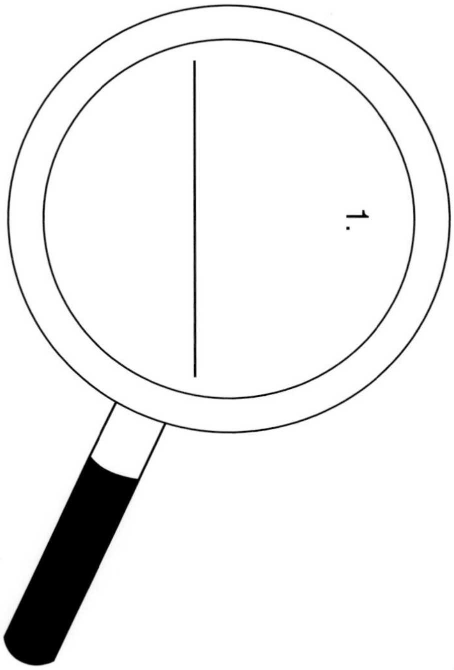

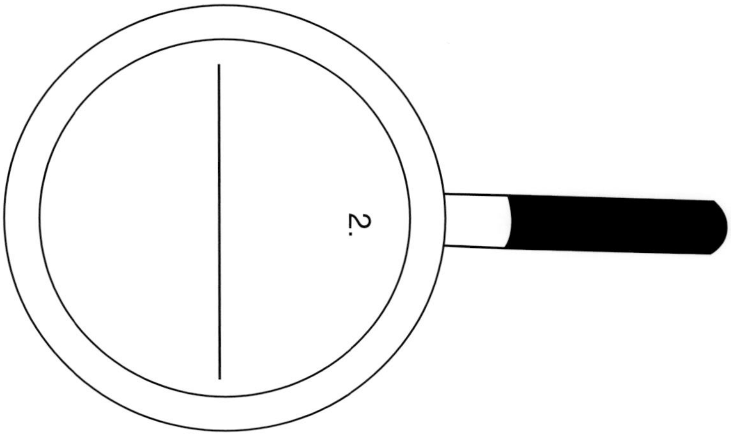

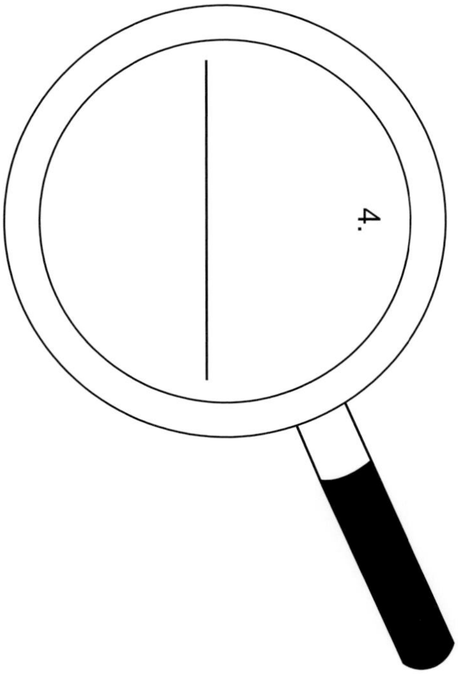

Name: ______________________________

1.

2.

3.

4.

Name: ______________________________

Summer	Fall
Winter	Spring

Name: ______________________________

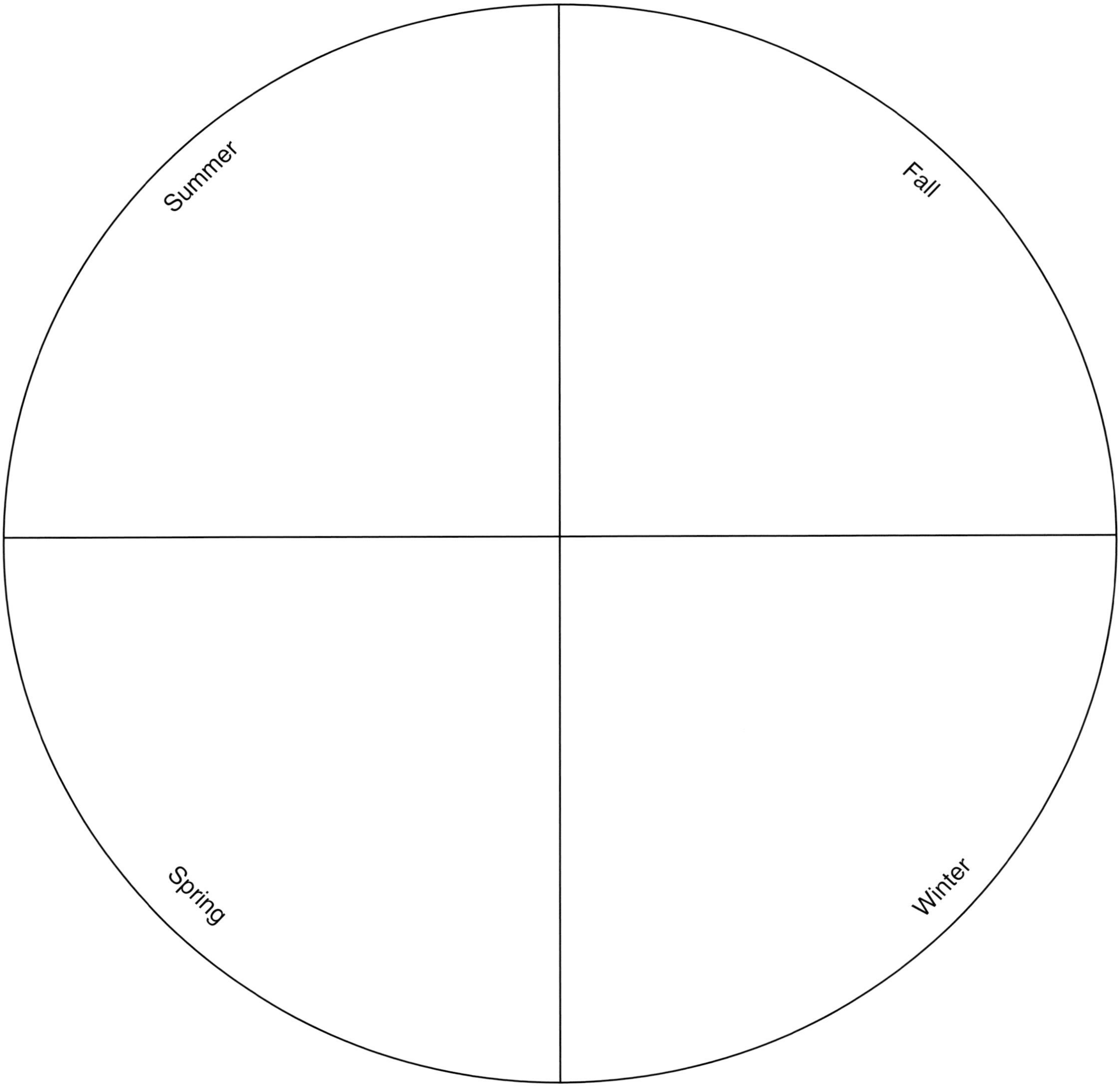

Name: ____________________

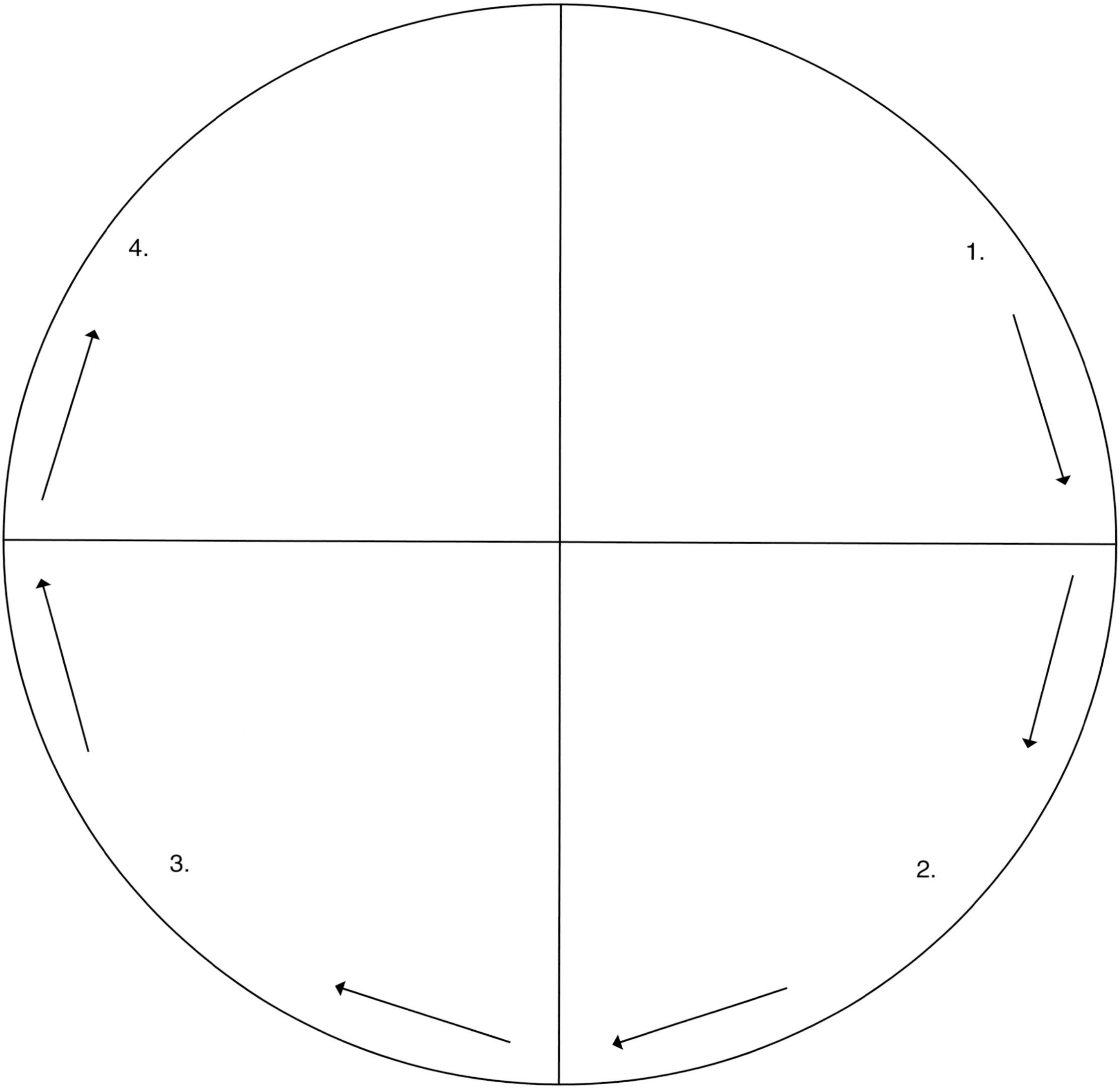

Name: ______________________

1.	2.	3.	4.

Name: ____________________

Steps	Details
Step 1:	
Step 2:	
Step 3:	
Step 4:	
Step 5:	

Name: ______________________________

1

2

3

4

5

6

Name: ______________________________

1.

2.

3.

4.

5.

6.

Name: ______________________________

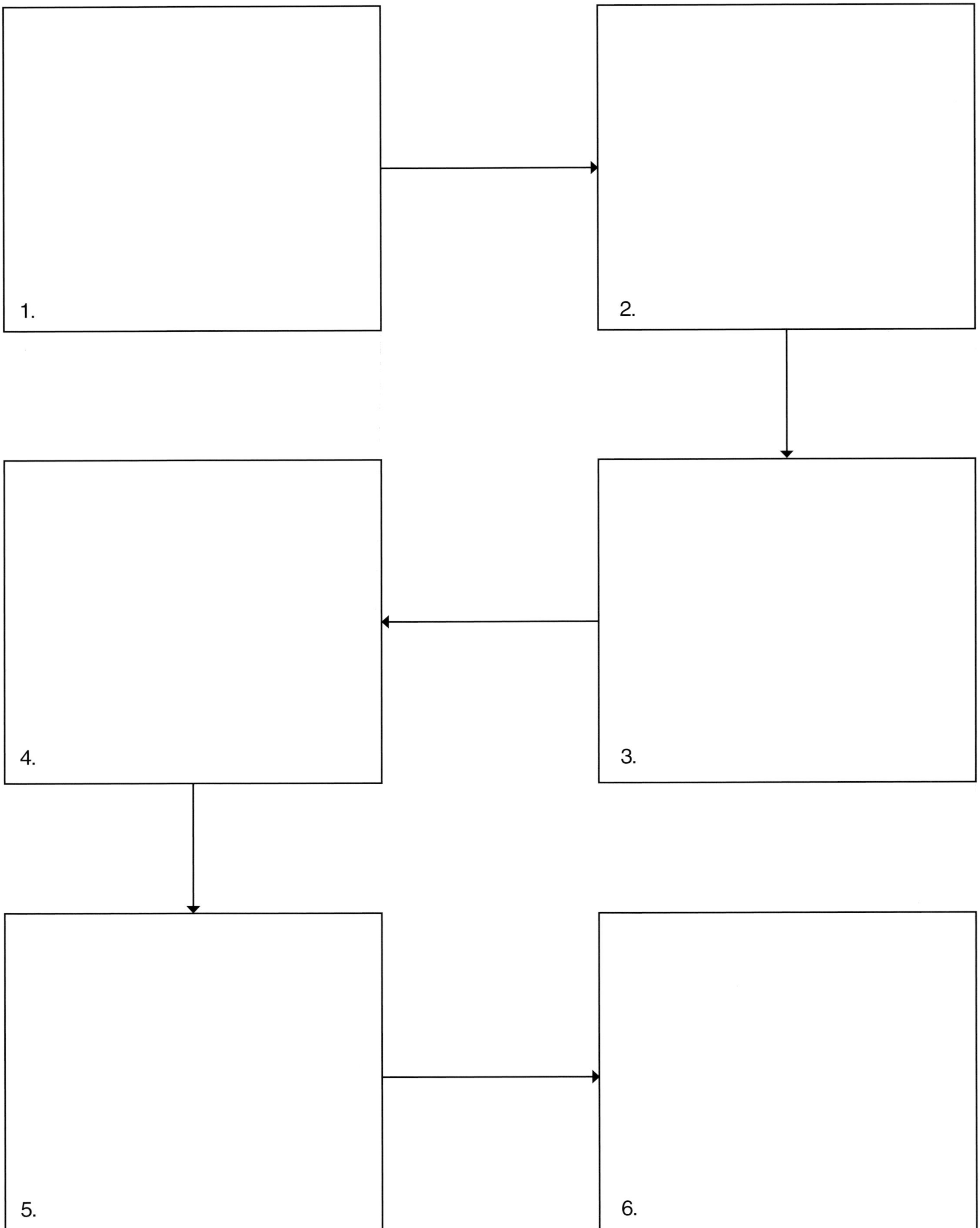

Name: ______________________

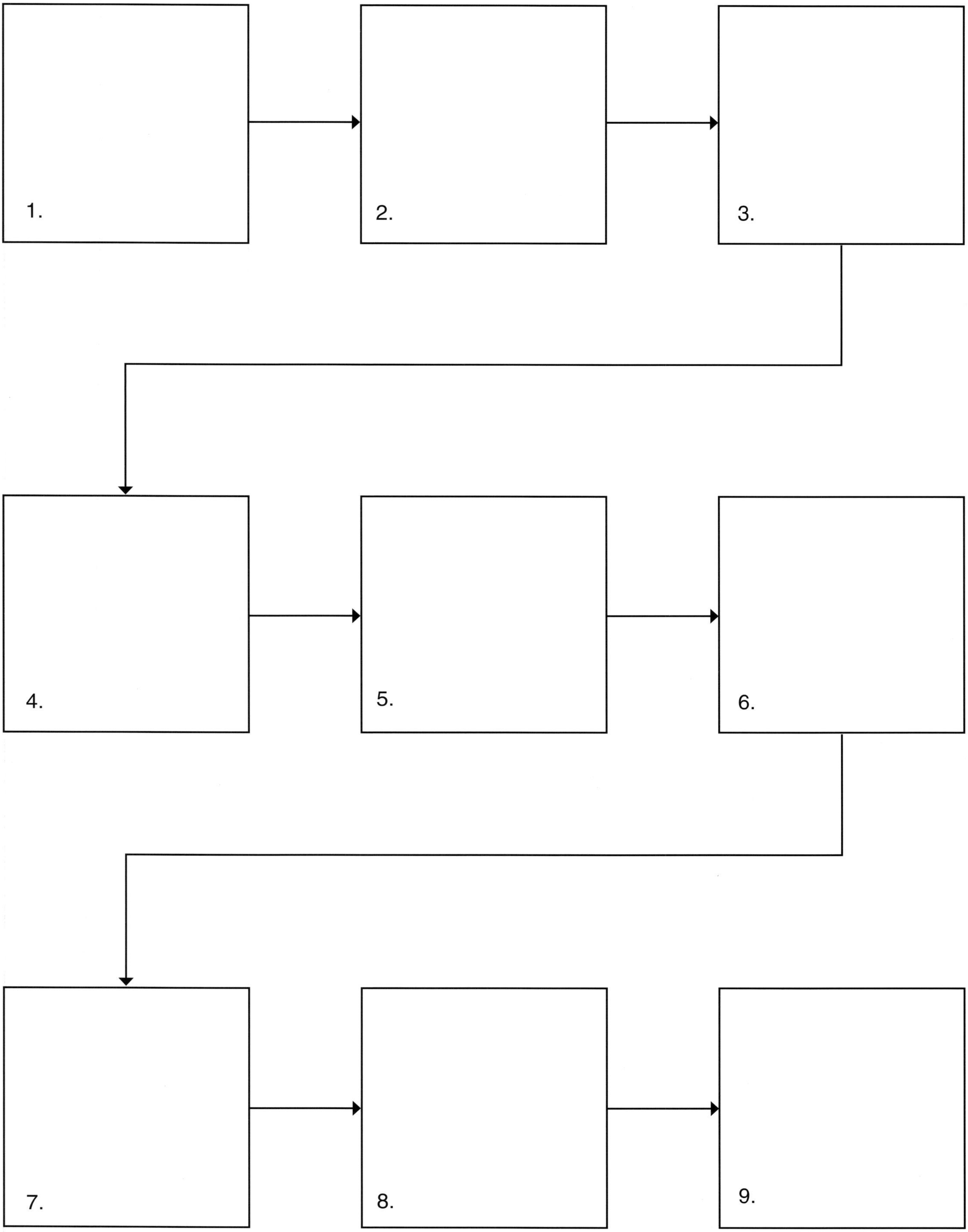

Name: ______________________________

A. ______________________

1.

2.

3.

4.

5.

B. ______________________

1.

2.

3.

4.

5.

6.

7.

Name: ____________________

1.	2.
3.	4.
5.	6.
7.	8.
9.	10.

Name: ______________________________

	Date	Occurrence	Qualifier	Additional Info.
Event				
Event				
Event				
Event				
Event				
Event				

Name: ______________________________

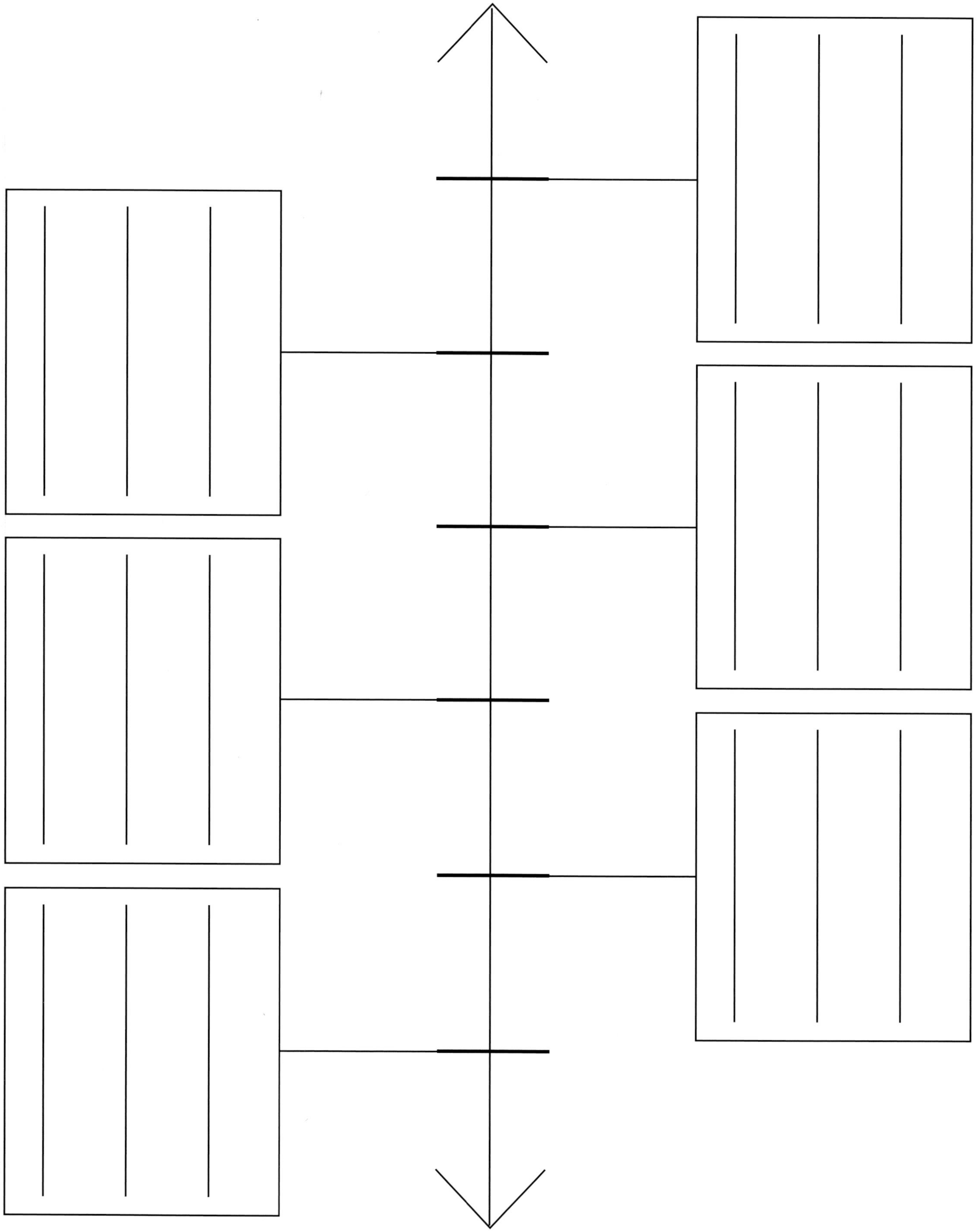

Name: ______

Name: ______________________________

Name: ______________________________

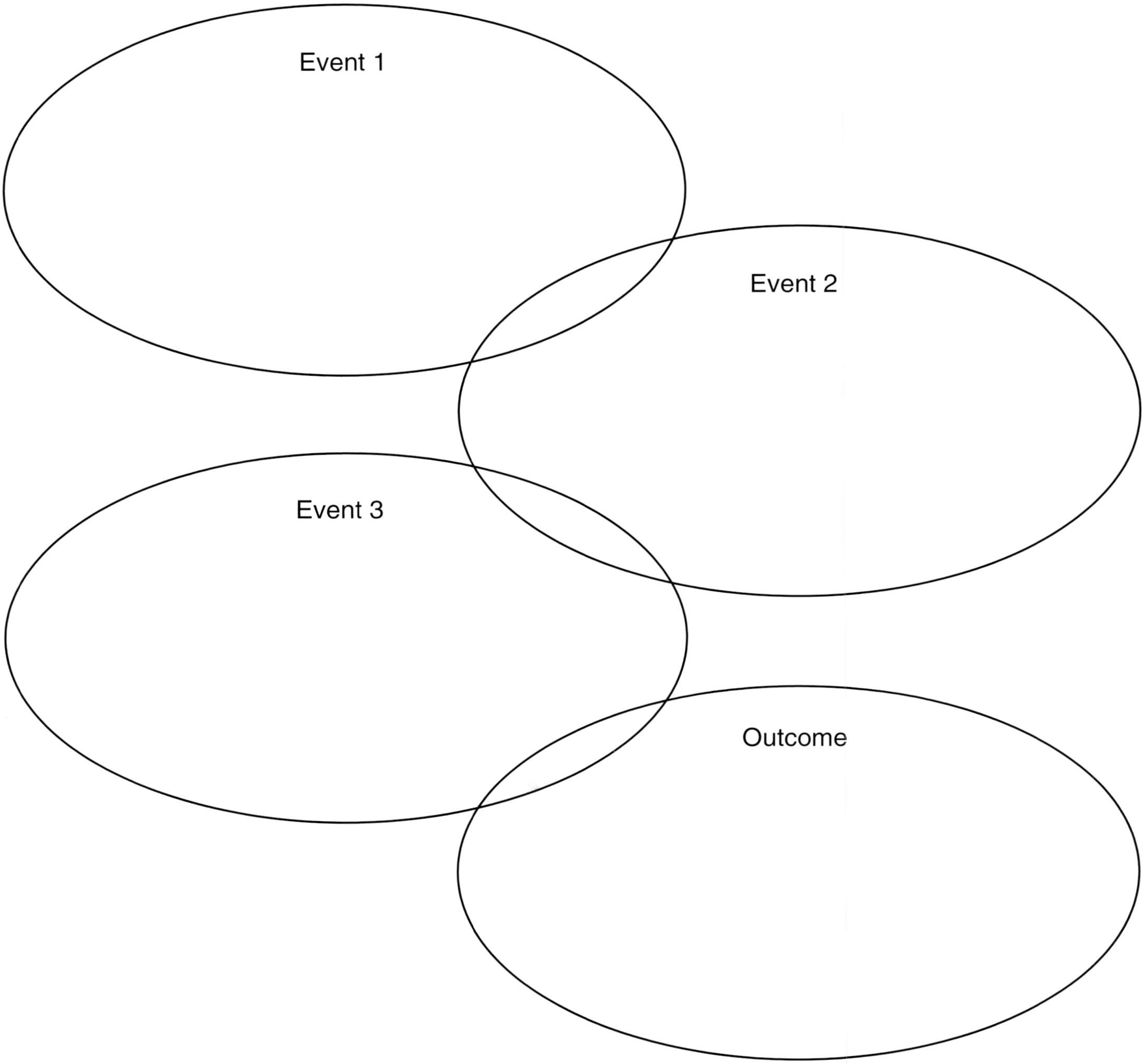

Name: ______________________

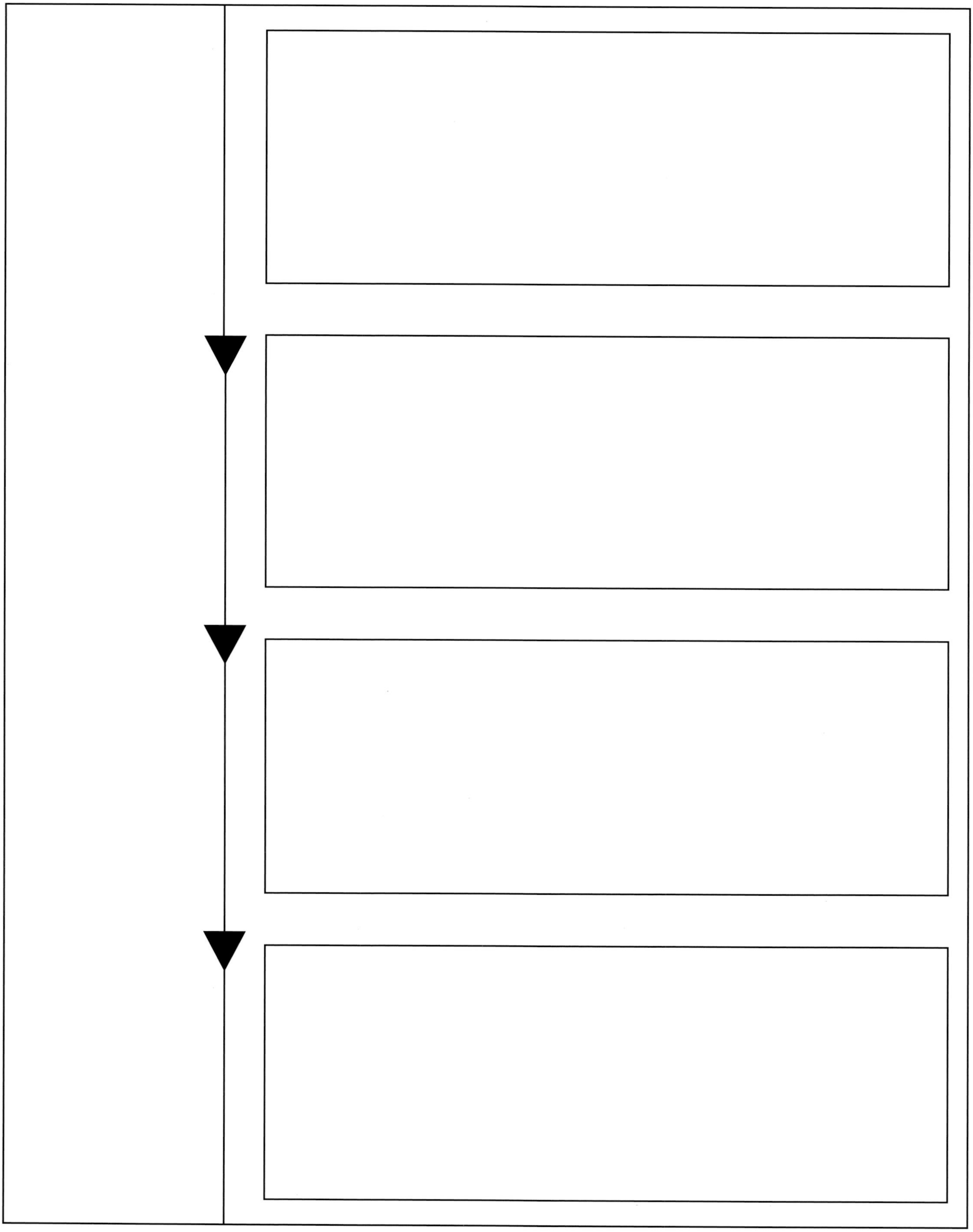

Name: ______________________

Name: ____________________

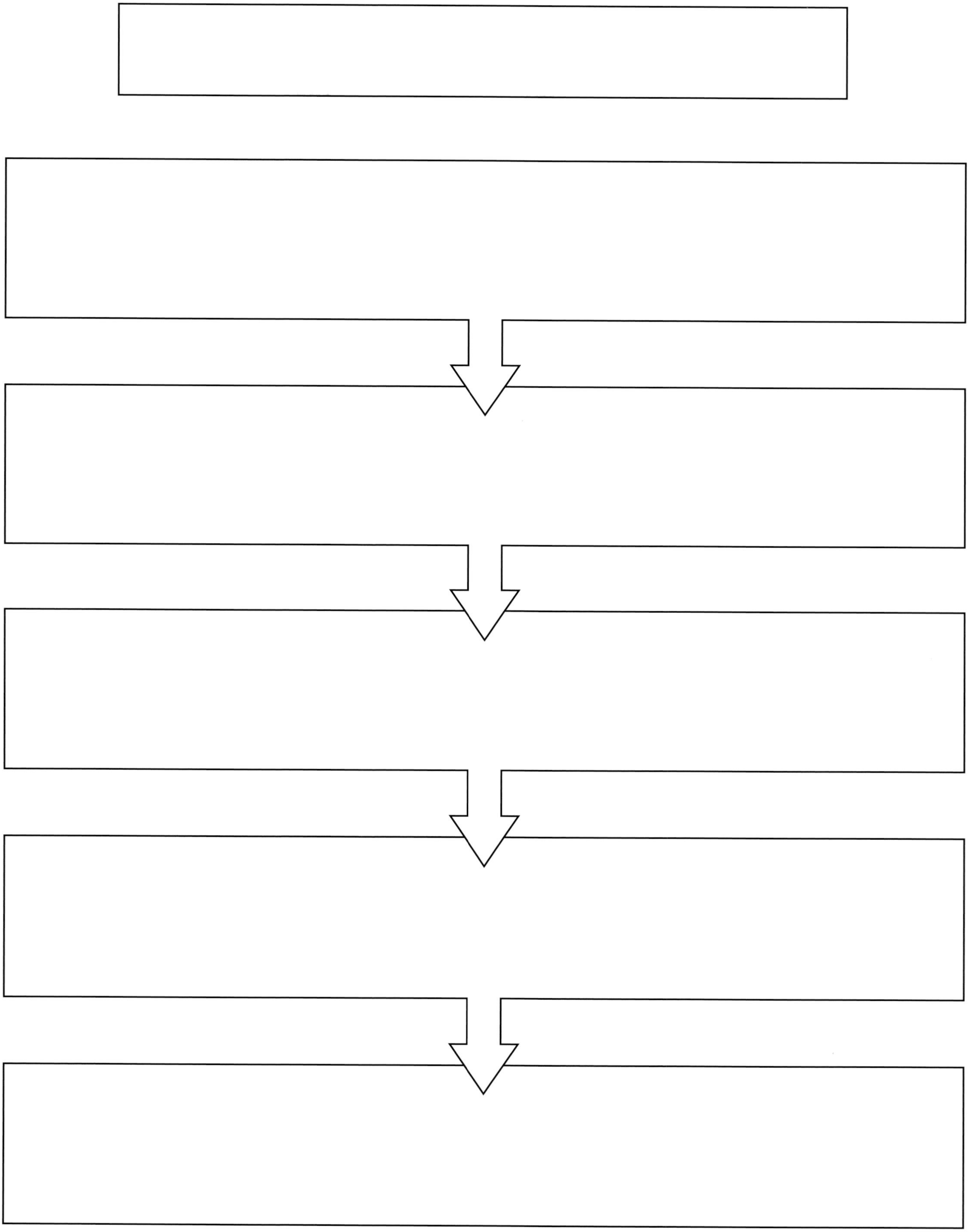

Name: ______________________________

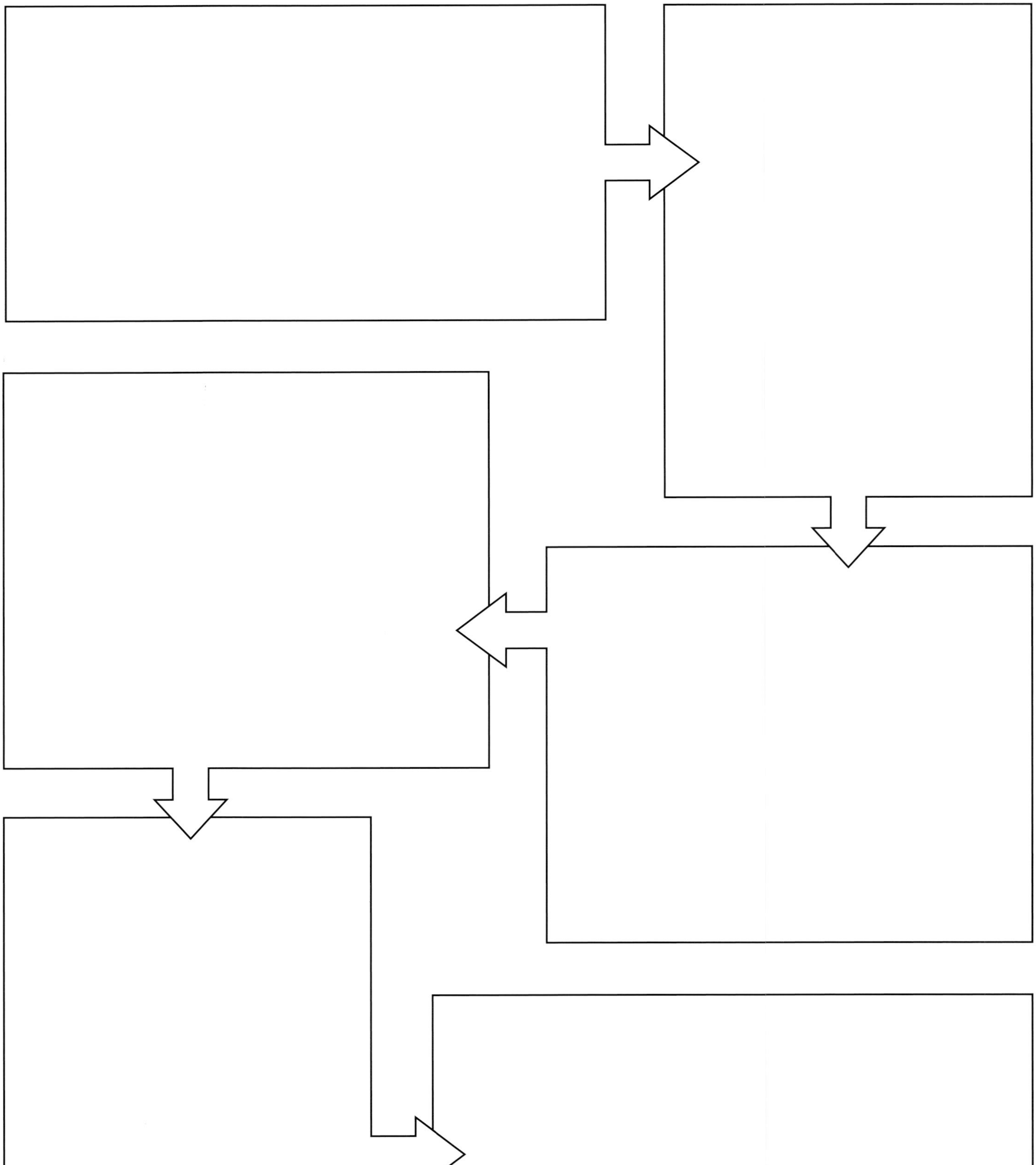

Name: ______________________________

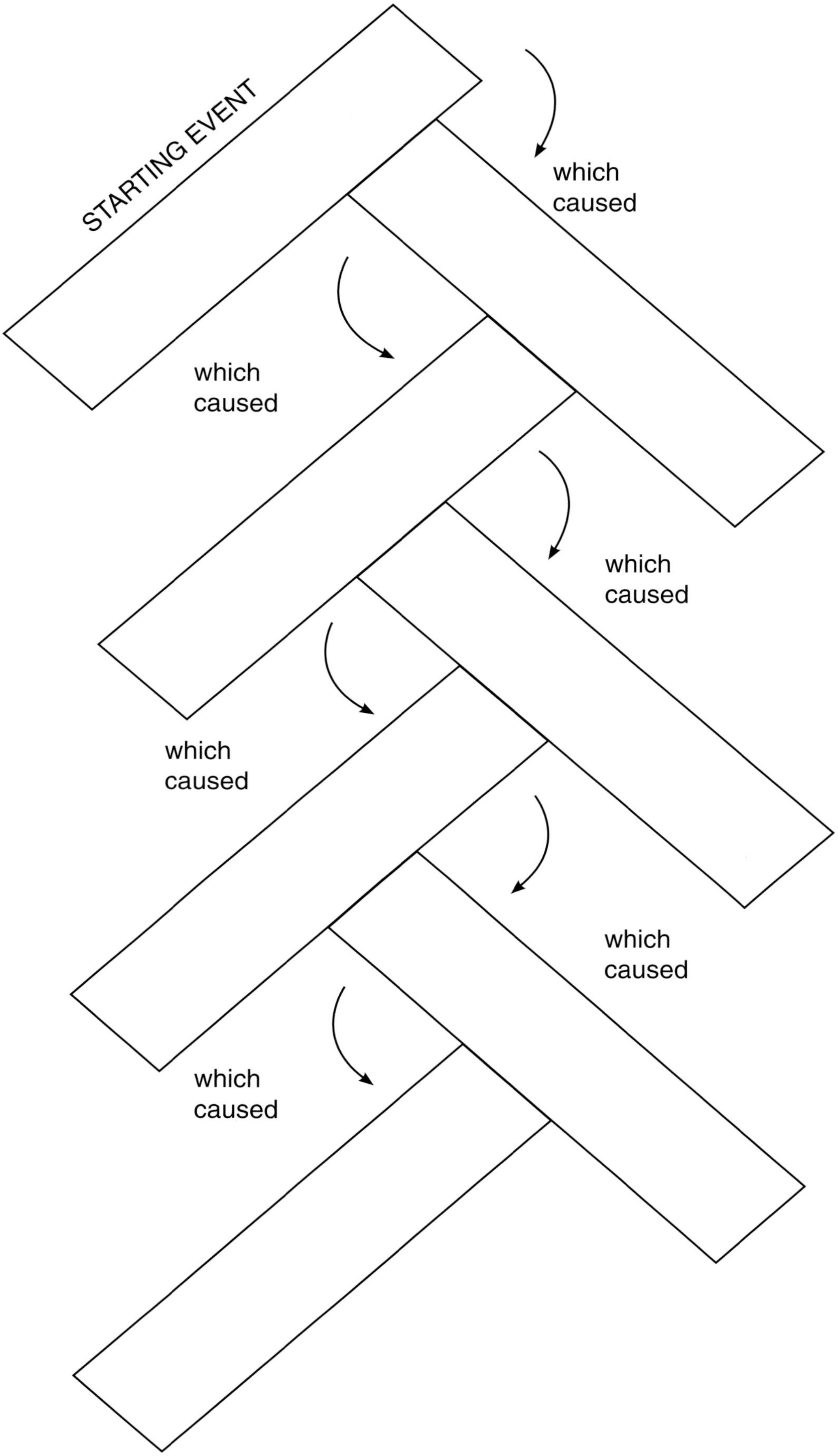

STARTING EVENT
which caused
which caused
which caused
which caused
which caused
which caused

Name: ______________________________

Name: ______________________________

Cause

Effect

Cause

Effect

Cause

Effect

Name: ______________________________

Name: ____________________

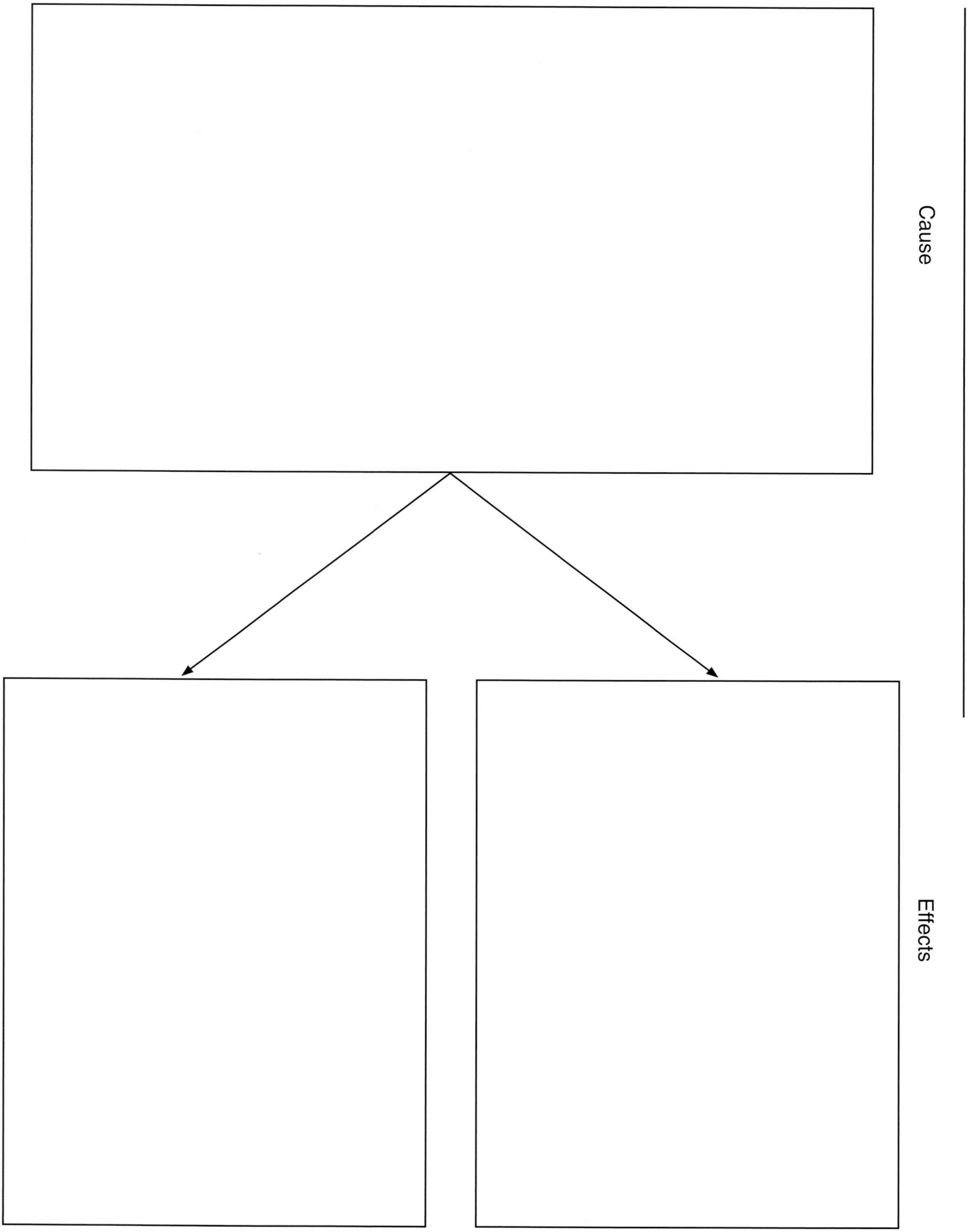

Name: ______________________________

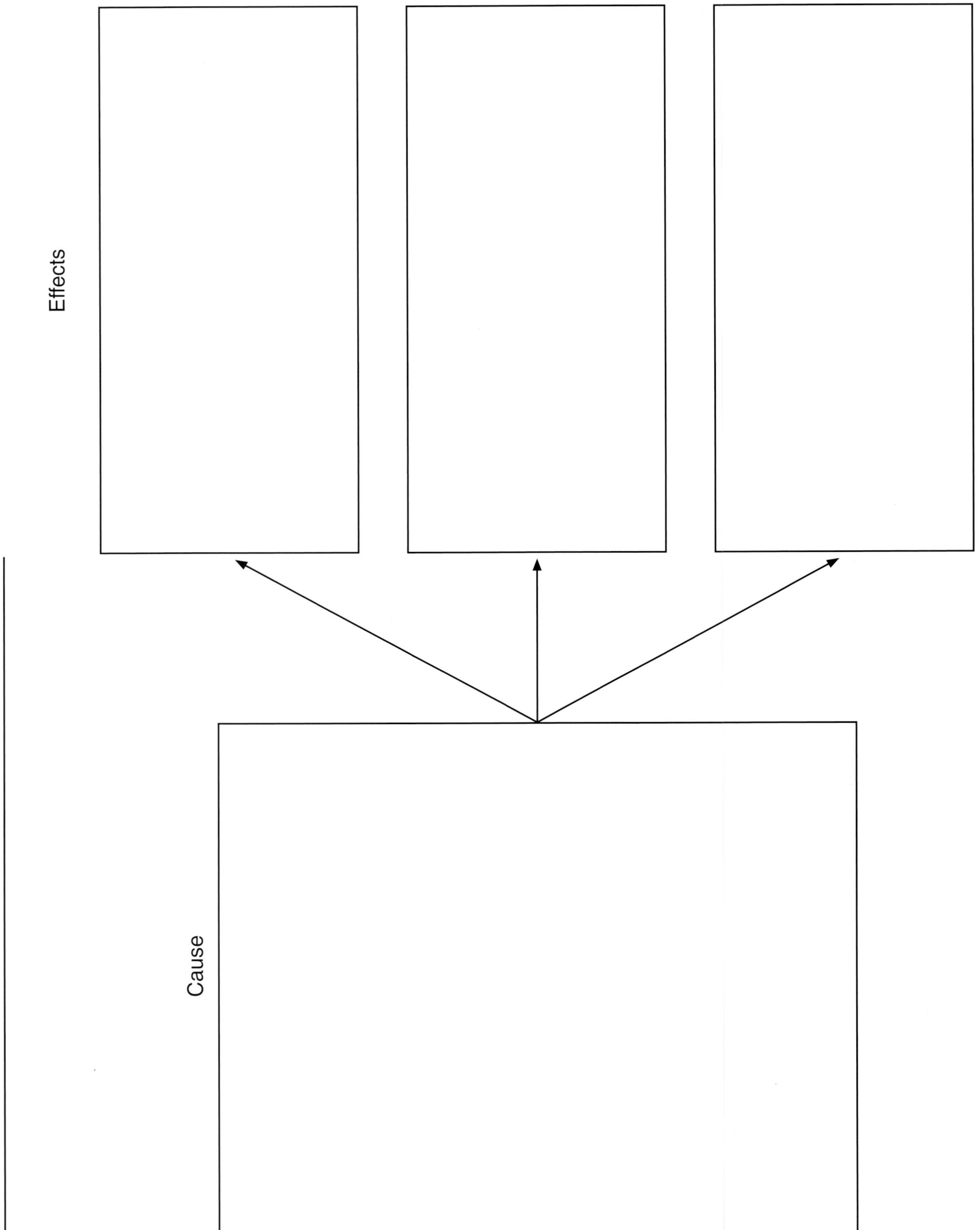

Name: ____________________

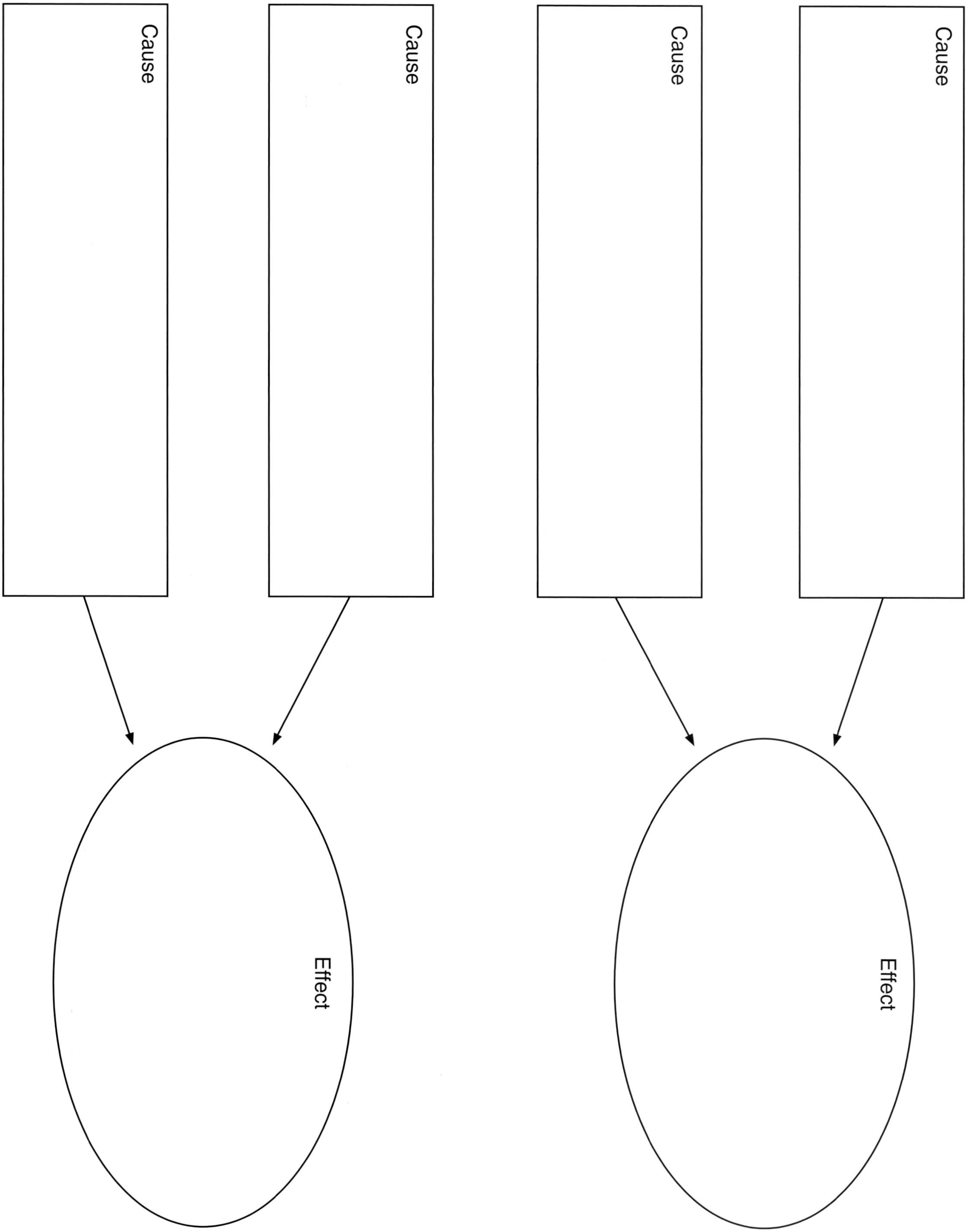

Name: ______________________________

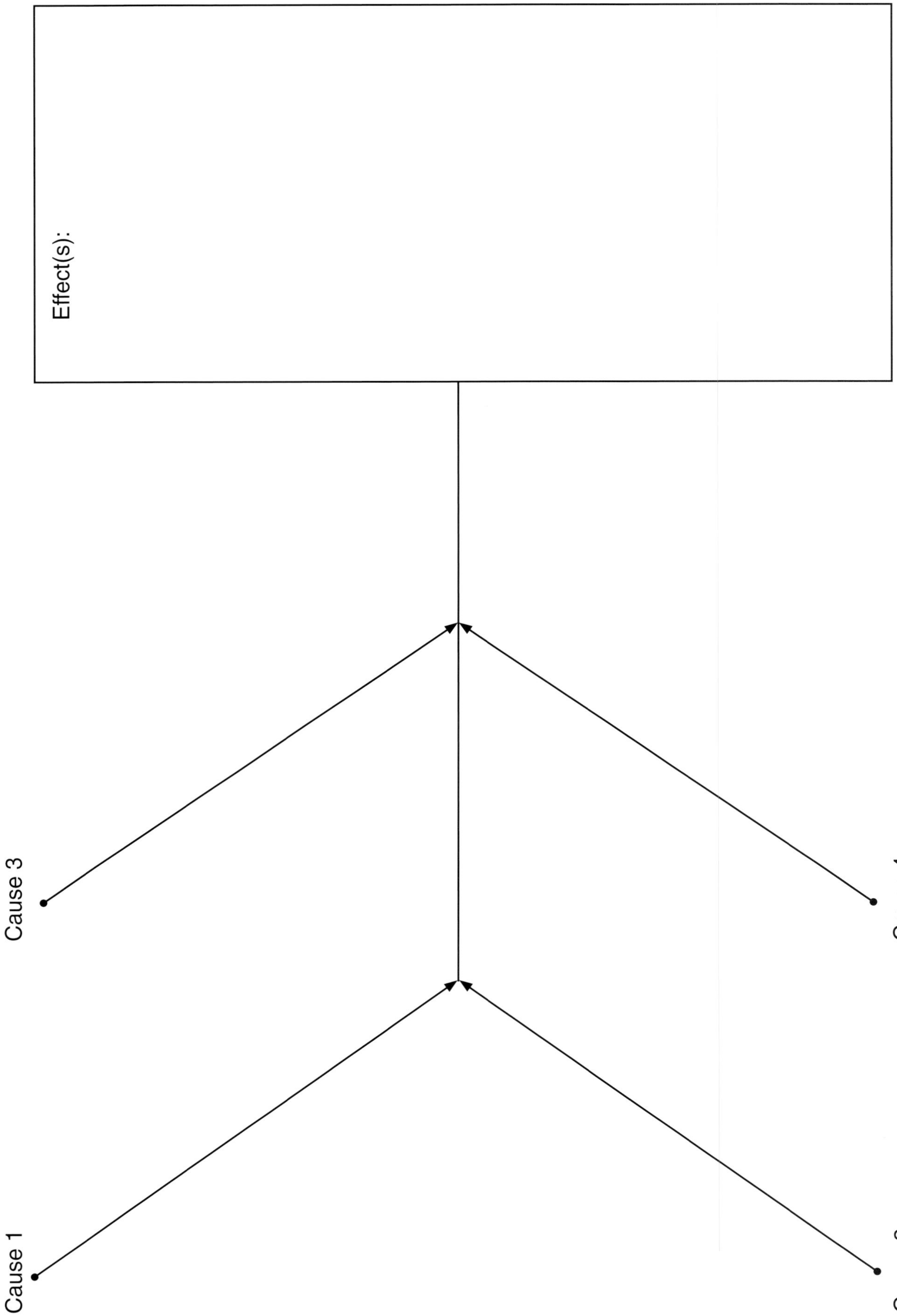

Name: ____________________

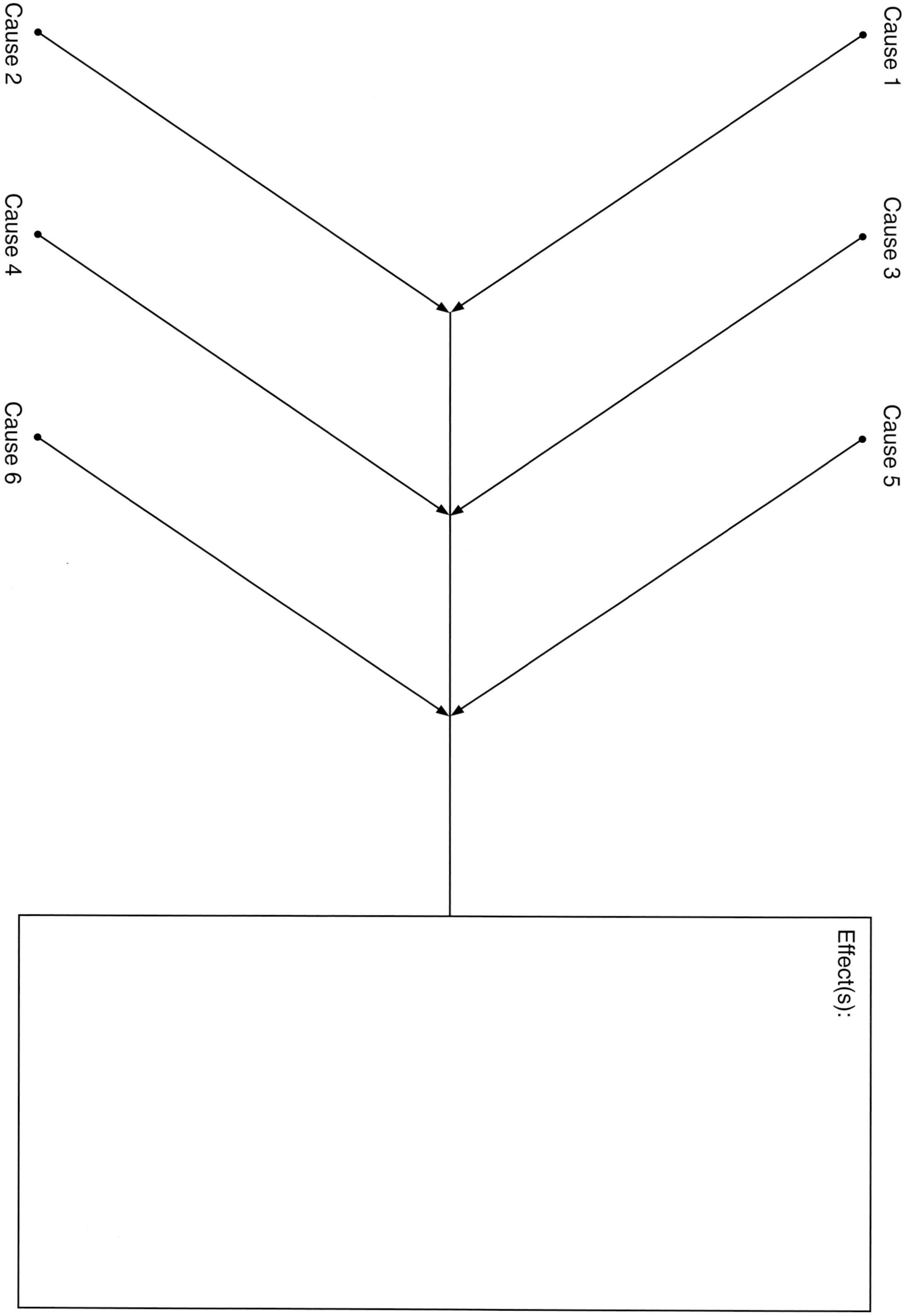

Name: ______________________________

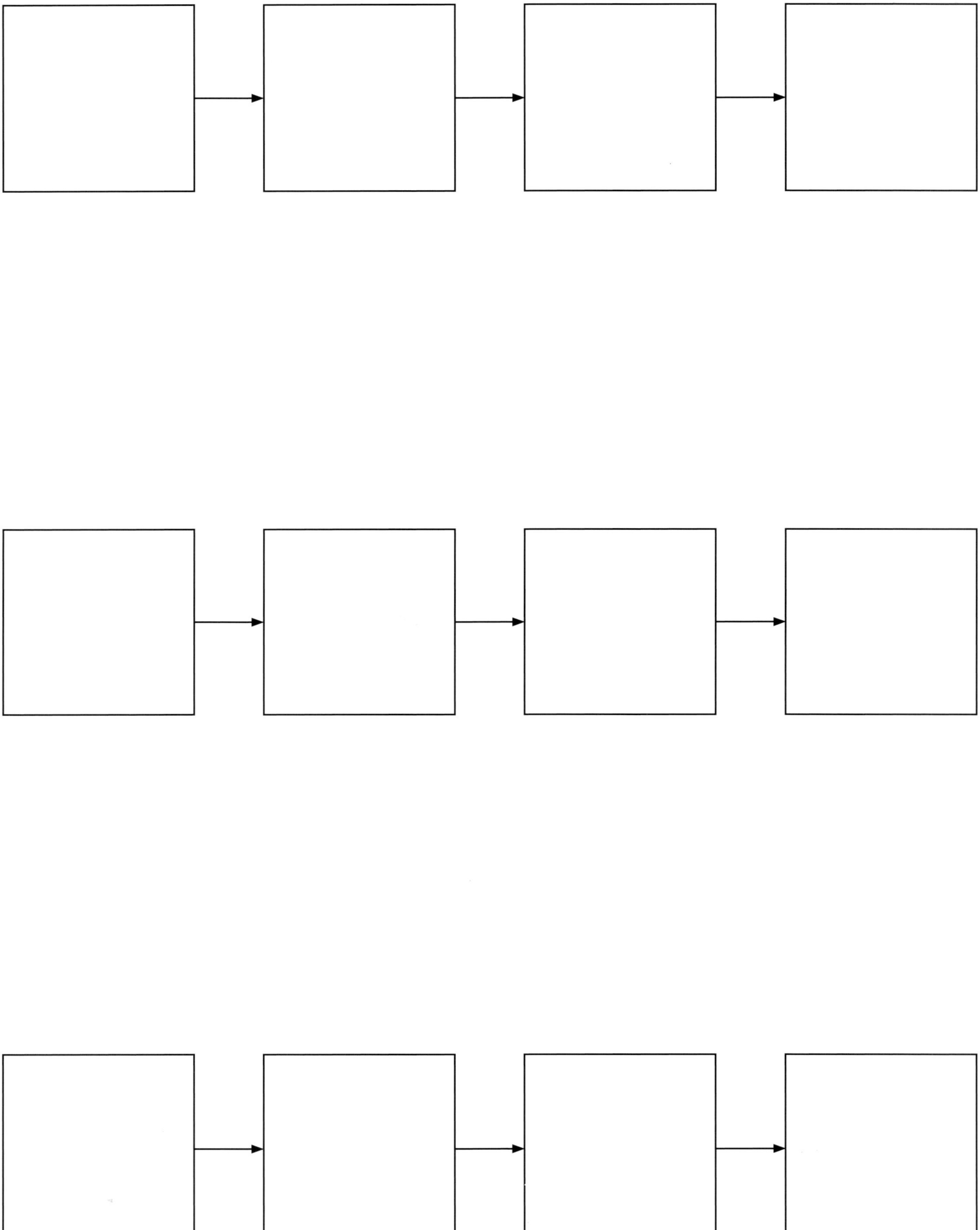

Name: ______________________________

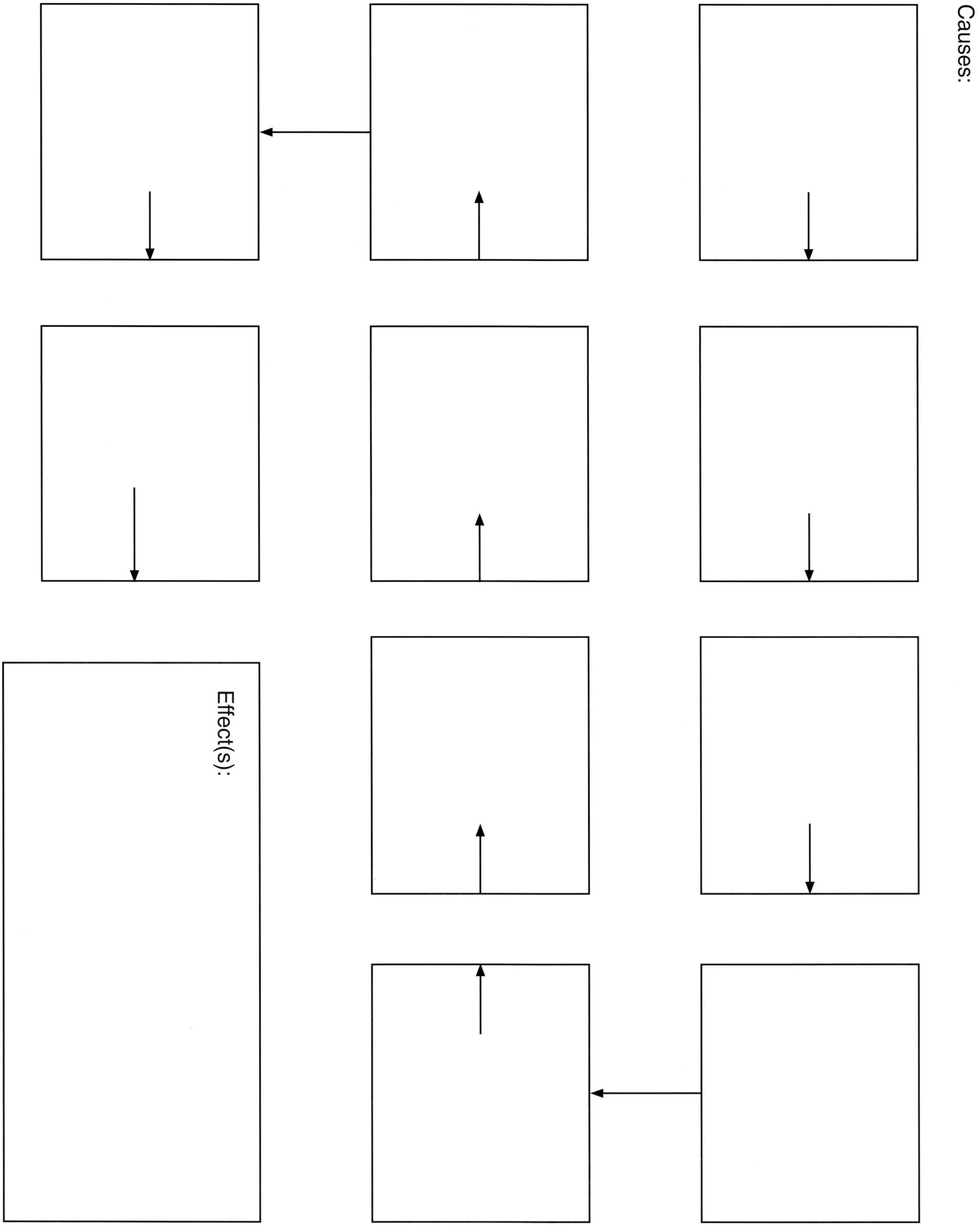

Name: ____________________

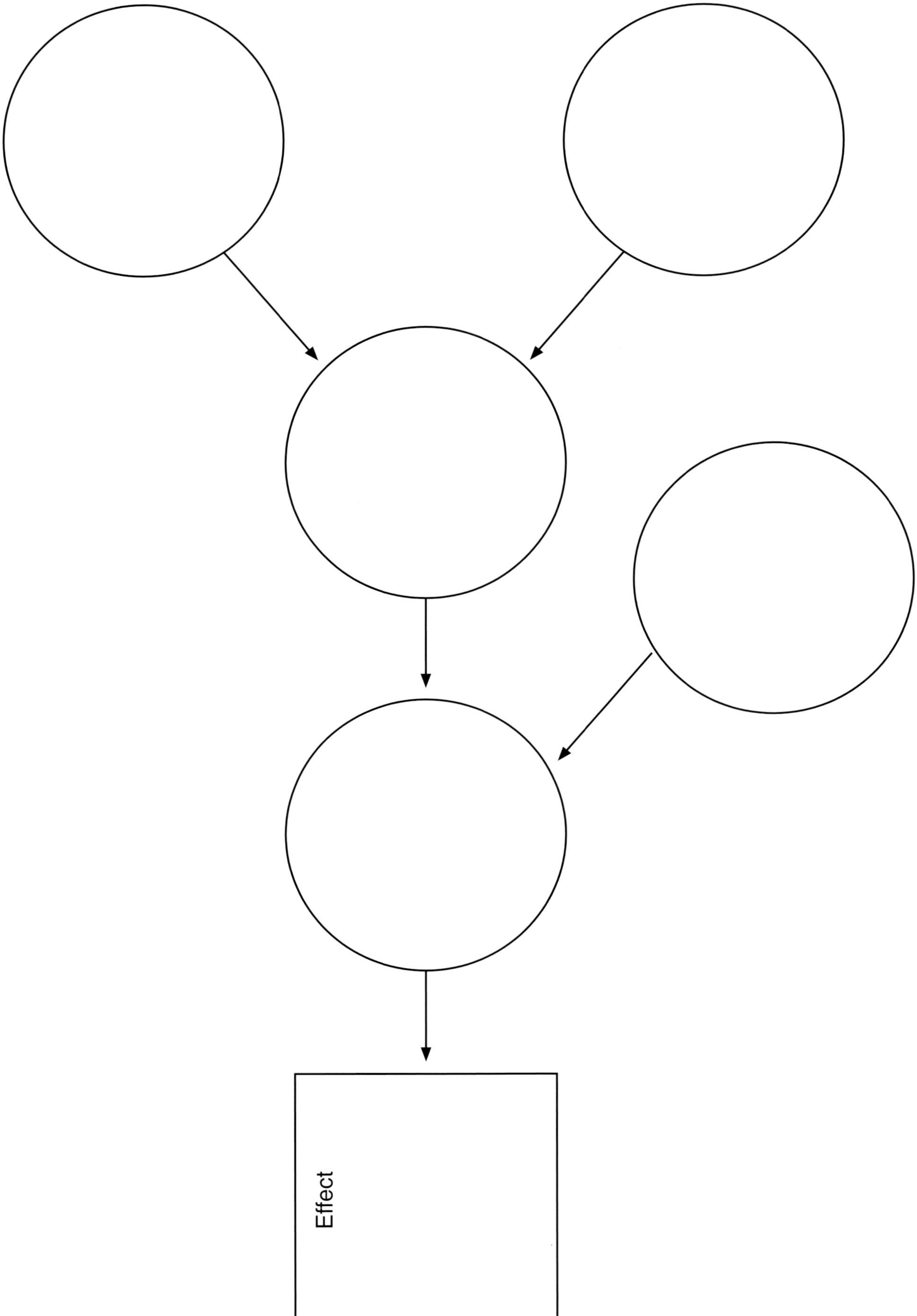

Name: ______________________________

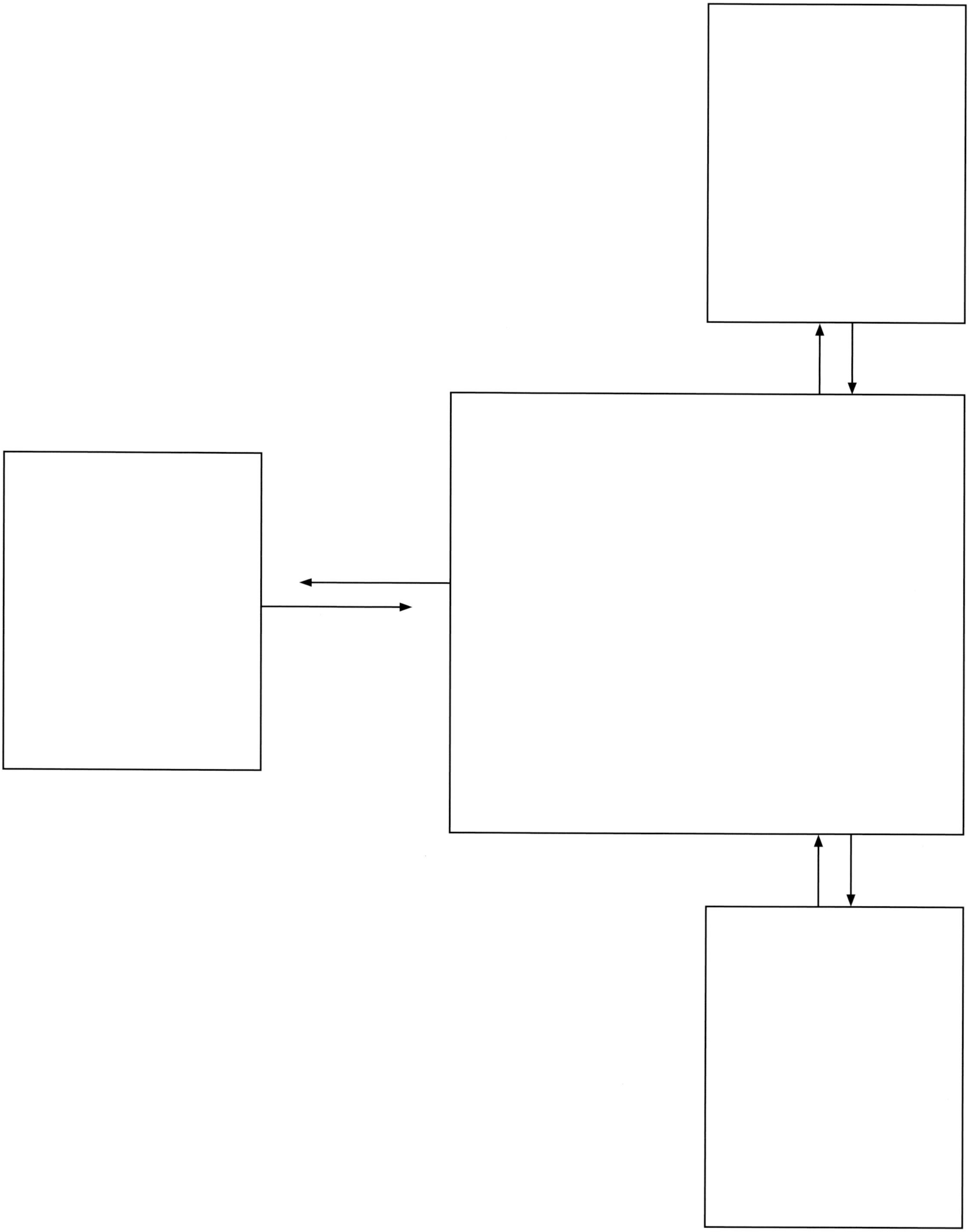

Name: ______________________________

Name: ______________________________

1. A → B

2. A → B

3. A → B

4. A → B

Name: ______________________________

Name: ____________________

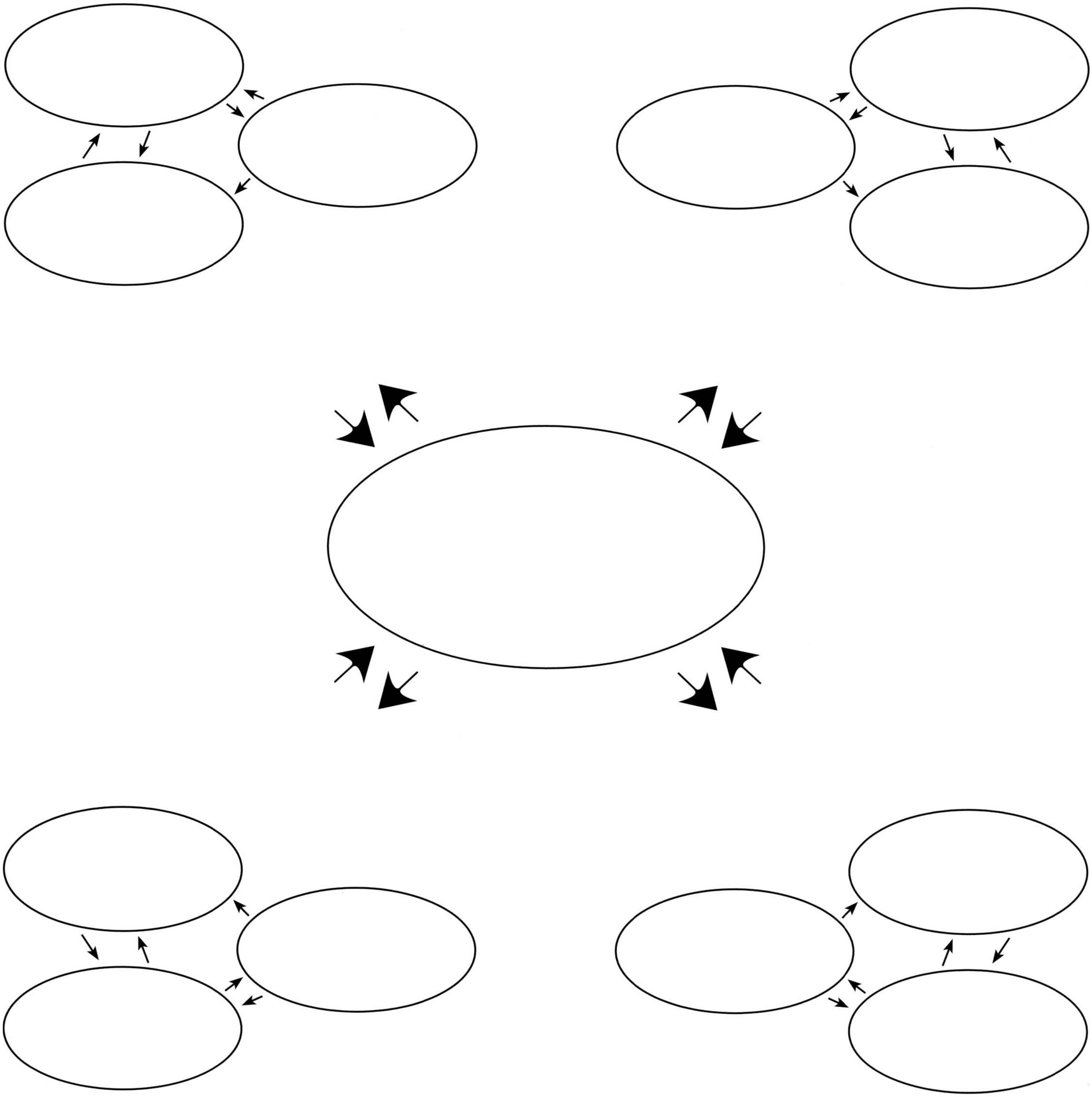

Name: ______________________________

What Happened...	What Could Happen Because of This?

Name: ________________________________

Prediction:

Facts	Cause/Effect Prediction	Patterns	Analysis

Name: ____________________

Situation Beforehand

1)
2)
3)
4)

Important Chain of Events

1)

2)

3)

4)

5)

6)

7)

8)

Effect 1

Effect 2

Effect 3

Long-term Consequences

What If...

1)

2)

3)

4)

5)

6)

7)

8)

Effect 1

Effect 2

Effect 3

Long-term Consequences

Name: ____________________

See	Hear
Feel	Smell

Name: ______________________________

Describing Words

Looks Like	Sounds Like	Feels Like	Smells Like	Tastes Like

Name: ______________________________

Observation(s): ______________________________

____

____

Describing Words

Color	Size
Taste	Number
Smell	Looks
Texture	Sounds
Shape	Other

Name: ______________________________

Oject	
Sight	
Sound	
Smell	
Taste	
Feel/Texture	
Additional Information	

Name: ____________________

Item	Looks	Feels	Smells	Sounds	Tastes

Name: ____________________

Topic ____________________

What I Know	What I Want to Know	What I Learned

Name: ____________________

Topic ____________________		
What I Know	What I Want to Know	Possible Sources

Name: ______________________________

What I know I know:

What I think I know:

What I think I'll learn:

What I know I learned:

Name: ______________________________

Name: ______________________________

Who?

What?

How?

Why?

When?

Where?

Name: ______________________________

Topic

Text Question (Context Connection)

Text Question (Context Connection)

Personal Question (Connection to Self)

Personal Question (Connection to Self)

Name: ____________________

Main Question

Sub-Question 1

Sub-Question 2

Sub-Question 3

Sub-Question 4

Sub-Question 5

Sub-Question 6

Name: ______________________________

Topic :

REFERENCES:

1.

2.

3.

4.

QUESTIONS:

1.

2.

3.

4.

Name: ______________________

Topic :

QUESTION I

NOTE-TAKING:

Name: ____________________

Topic :

QUESTION 2

NOTE-TAKING:

Name: ______________________________

Topic :

QUESTION 3

NOTE-TAKING:

Name: ______________________________

Topic :

QUESTION 4

NOTE-TAKING:

Name: ____________________

Author: ____________________

Title: ____________________

Place of Publication: ____________________

Publisher: ____________________

Date of Publication: ____________________

Notes in your own words:

Quotes:

Name: ______________________________

Article Author: ______________________________

Article Title: ______________________________

Pages: ______________________________

Magazine Title: ______________________________

Date of Publication: ______________________________

Notes in your own words:

Quotes:

Name: ______________________________

Entry Title: ______________________________

Encyclopedia Title: ______________________________

Date of Publication: ______________________________

Notes in your own words:

Quotes:

Name: ______________________________

Web Page Title: ______________________________

Web Address: ______________________________

Date of last update if available: ______________________________

Date you last viewed the page: ______________________________

Notes in your own words:

Quotes:

Name: ______________________________

Research Question:

Vocabulary Words:

Vocabulary Word	Research Connection

Name: ____________________

Research Topic	1st Source	2nd Source	3rd Source
Question 1	Answer	Answer	Answer
Question 2			
Question 3			

Name: ____________________

Research Topic ______	1st Source	2nd Source	3rd Source	4th Source
Question 1	Answer	Answer	Answer	Answer
Question 2				
Question 3				

Name: ____________________

												Terminology
												Related term

Student-created definition:

Dictionary definition:

Student-created sentence:

Name: ____________________

Introduction Thesis Statement		
Topic Sentence	Topic Sentence	Topic Sentence
Details	Details	Details
Conclusion		
Notes		

Name: ______________________________

Summary	Response

Name: ______________________________

Prediction	
Question	

Name: ____________________

Prediction	Why	What Happened

Name: ________________________________

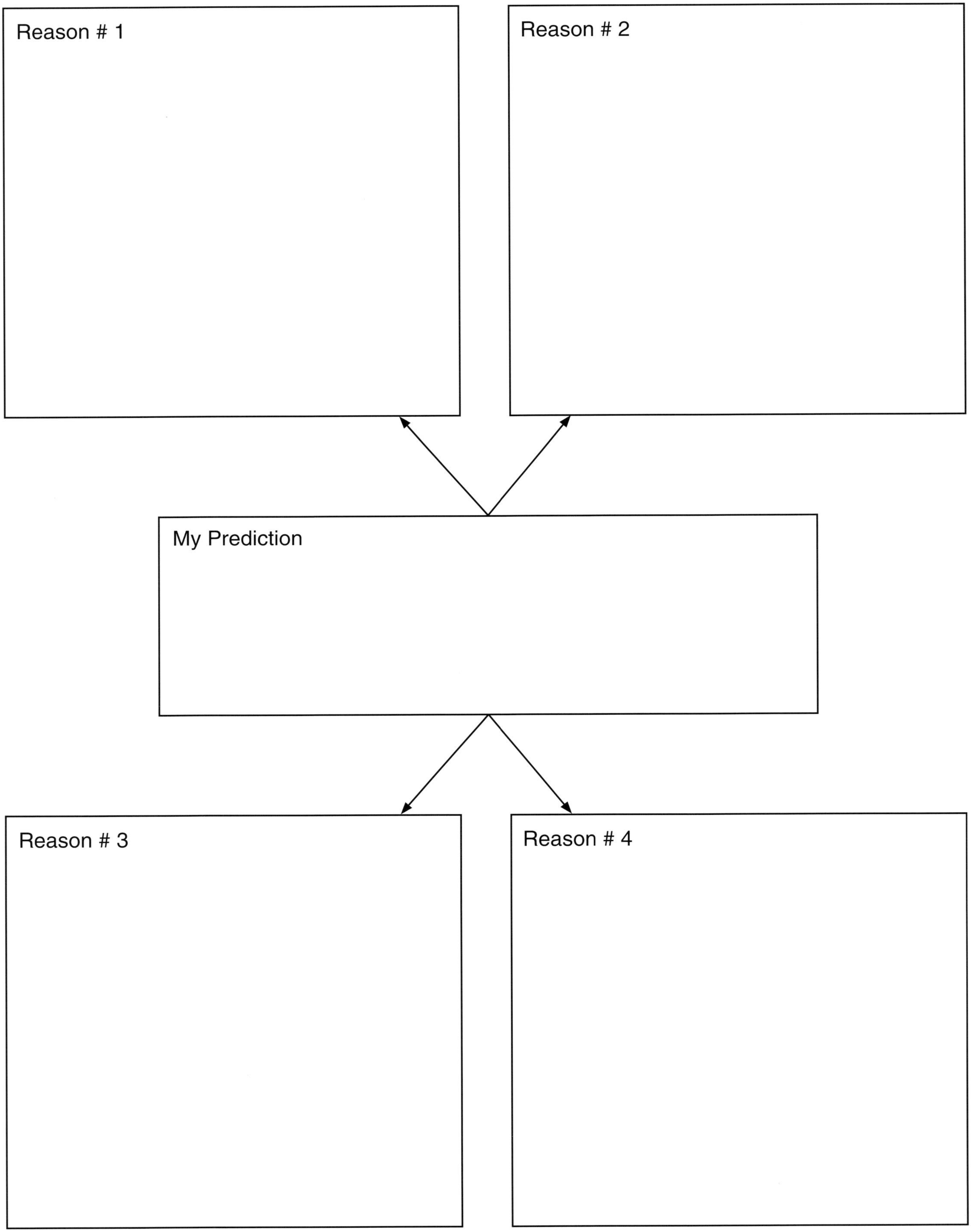

Name: ____________________

	Observation
	Hypothesis
	Prediction
	Experiment
	Conclusion

Name: ____________________

Question/Problem:

Hypothesis:

Experiment

Materials:

Procedure:

Results:

Conclusion:

Name: ____________________

Illustration

Set-up 1	Set-up 2

Results:

Results:

Variables in Set-up 1

Variables in Set-up 2

Constant Variables

Name: ______________________________

Discrepant Event:

Characteristics:

Vocabulary Association:

Real-life Examples:

Name: ______________________________

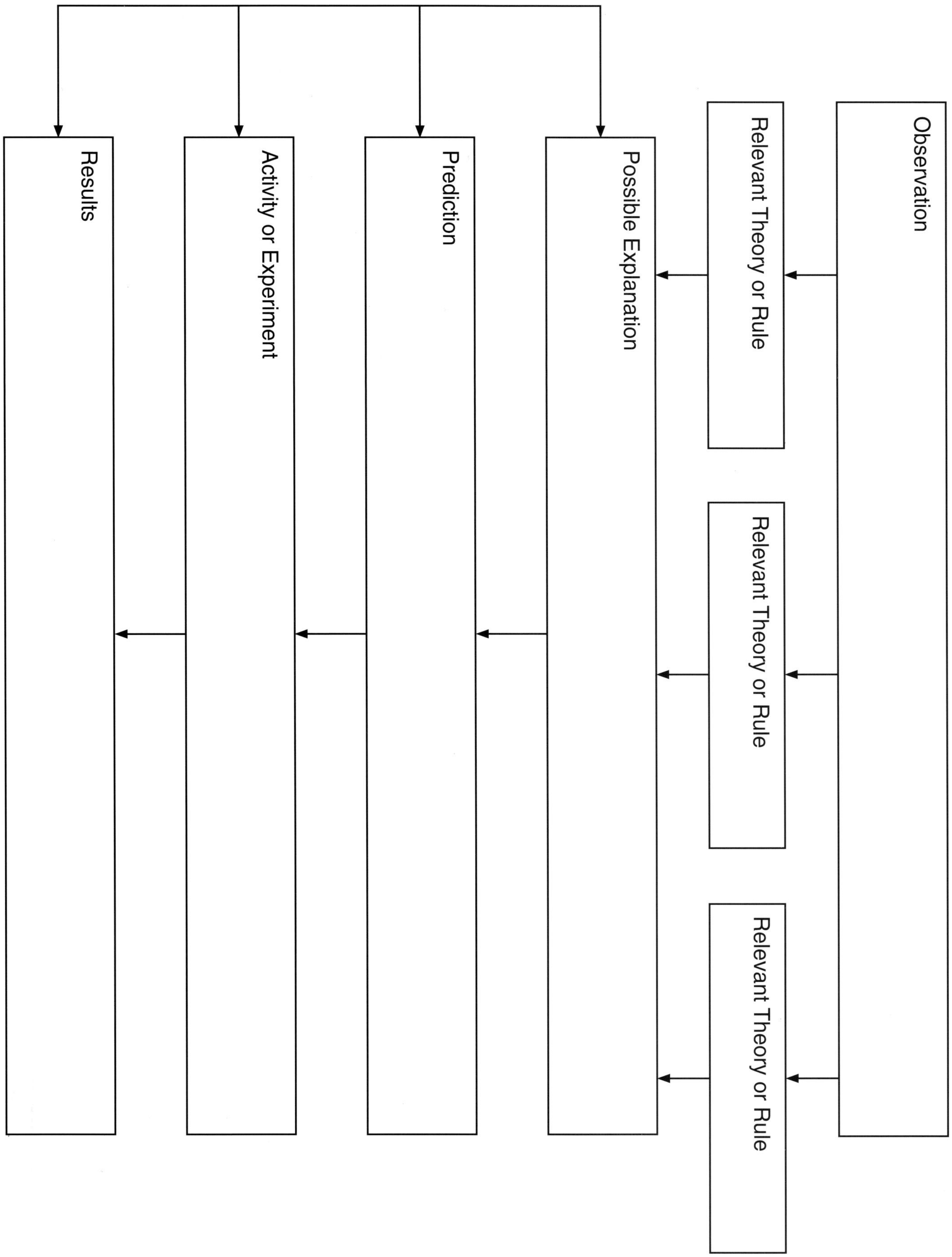
Observation
Relevant Theory or Rule
Relevant Theory or Rule
Relevant Theory or Rule
Possible Explanation
Prediction
Activity or Experiment
Results

Name: ____________________

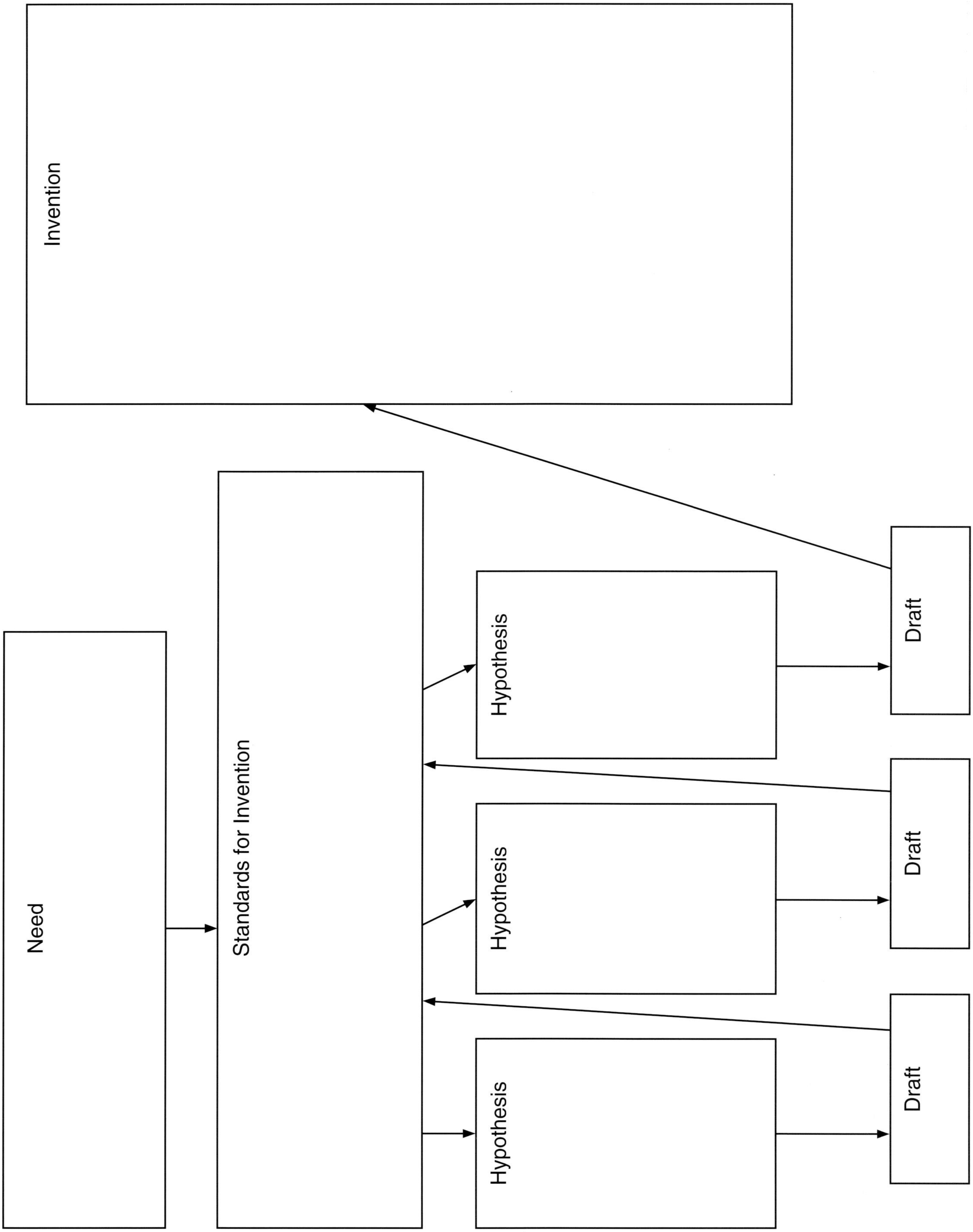
Invention
Need
Standards for Invention
Hypothesis
Hypothesis
Hypothesis
Draft
Draft
Draft

Name: ______________________

Need for the Invention:

Prior Uses:	Invented Uses:

Materials and Parts:

Illustration:

Name: ____________________

Topic: ____________________

1. ____________________

2. ____________________

3. ____________________

1. ____________________

2. ____________________

3. ____________________

1. ____________________

2. ____________________

3. ____________________

1. ____________________

2. ____________________

3. ____________________

Name: ____________________

THREE things I learned:

1.
2.
3.

TWO things that surprised me:

1.
2.

ONE question I have:

1.

Summary:

Resource Title:
Source:
Page Number(s)

Name: ______________________________

Prior Knowledge About ____________________	New Knowledge About ____________________
1.	1.
2.	2.
3.	3.
4.	4.
5.	5.
6.	6.
7.	7.
8.	8.

Name: ____________________

What I Did	What I Learned	How Can I Use it?

Name: ______________________________

Note-Taking	Note-Making

Name: ____________________

Name: ____________________

Name: ______________________________

Name: ____________________

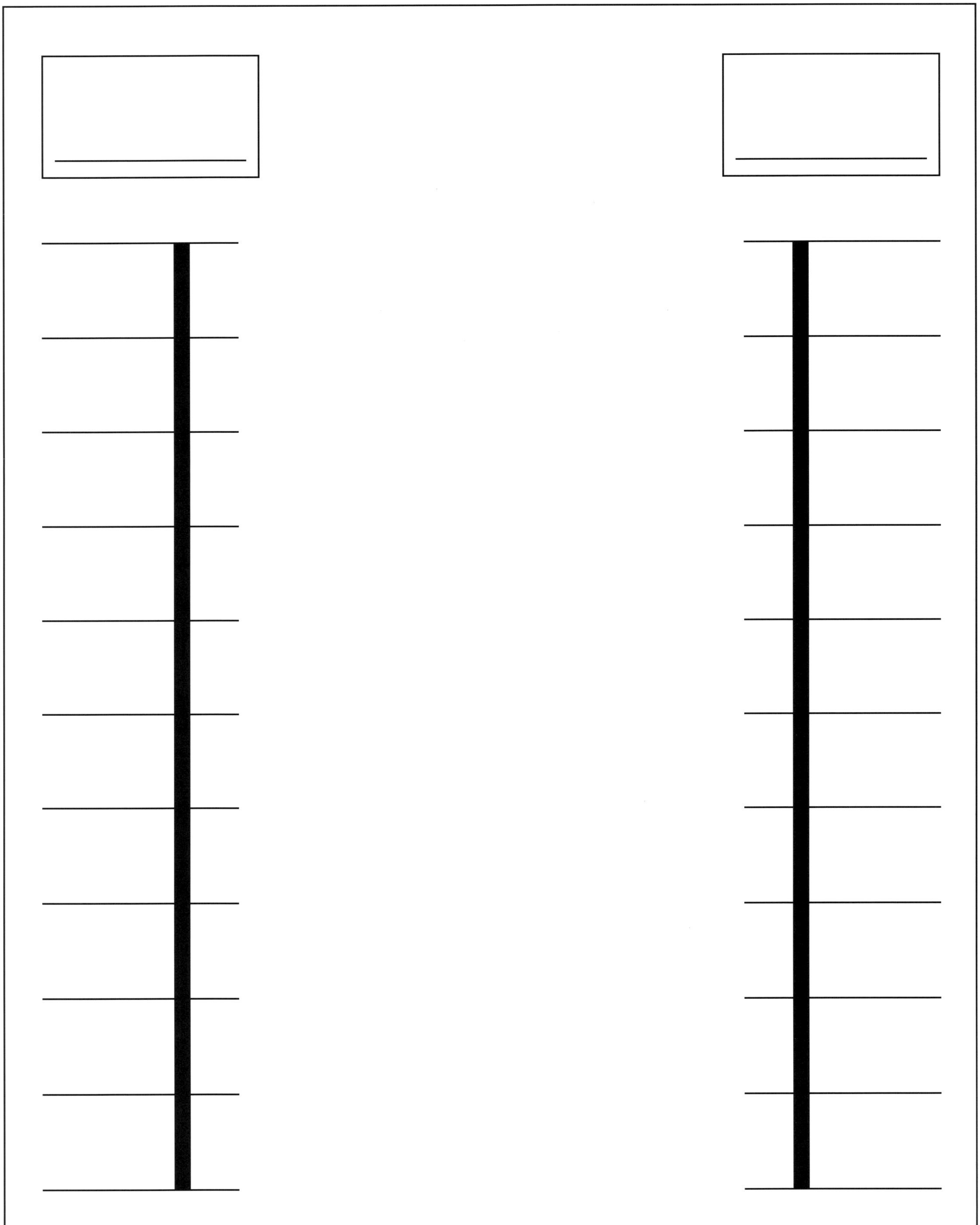

Name: ______________________

Name: ______________________________

Sun →	M →	T →	W →	Th →	F →	Sat

Name: ______________________________

Name: ______________________________

Name: ____________________

Name: ______________________________

Name: ______________________________

Name: ____________________

Name: ______________________________

Name: ____________________

Name: ____________________

Name: ____________________

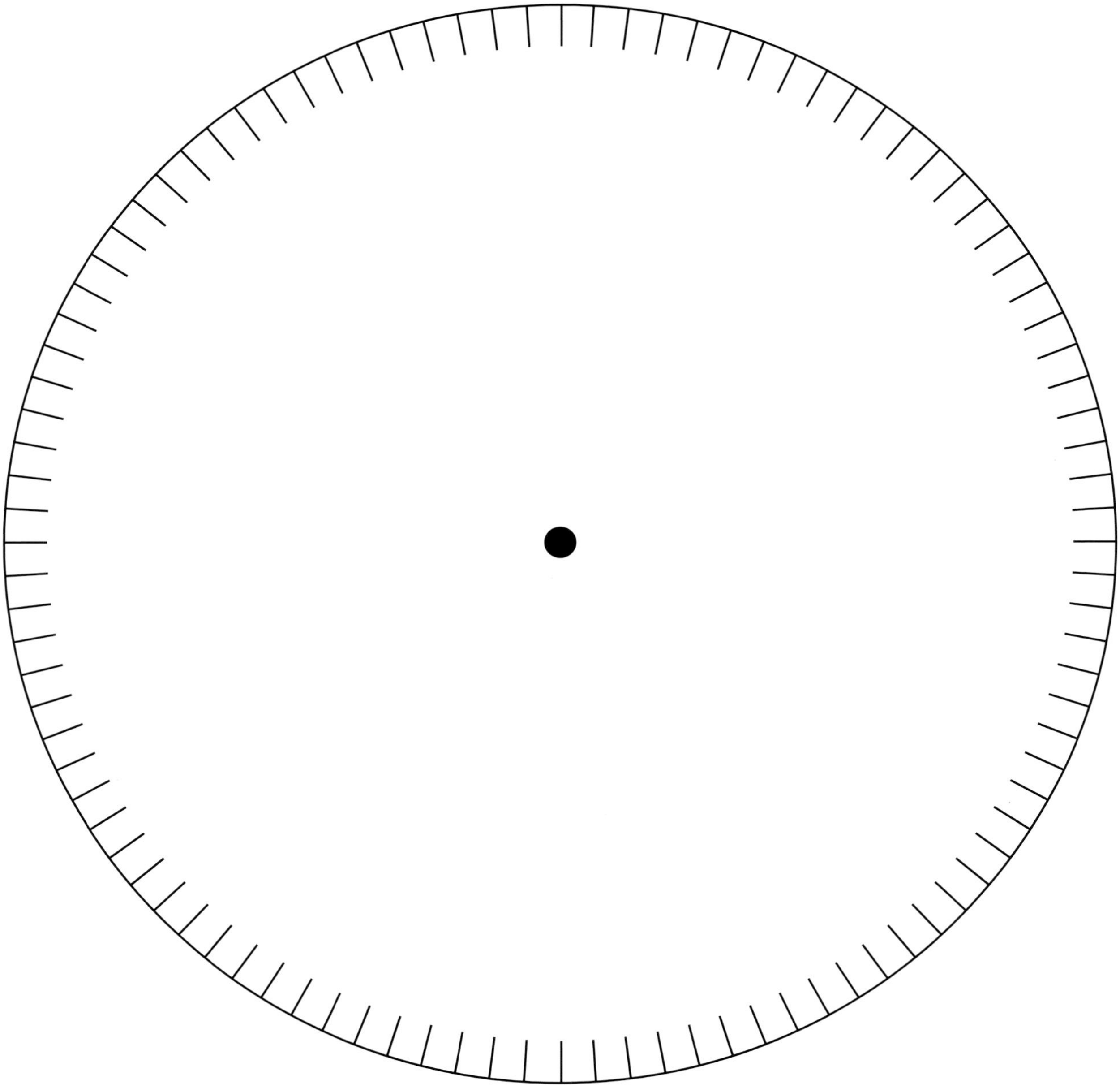

Name: ______________________________

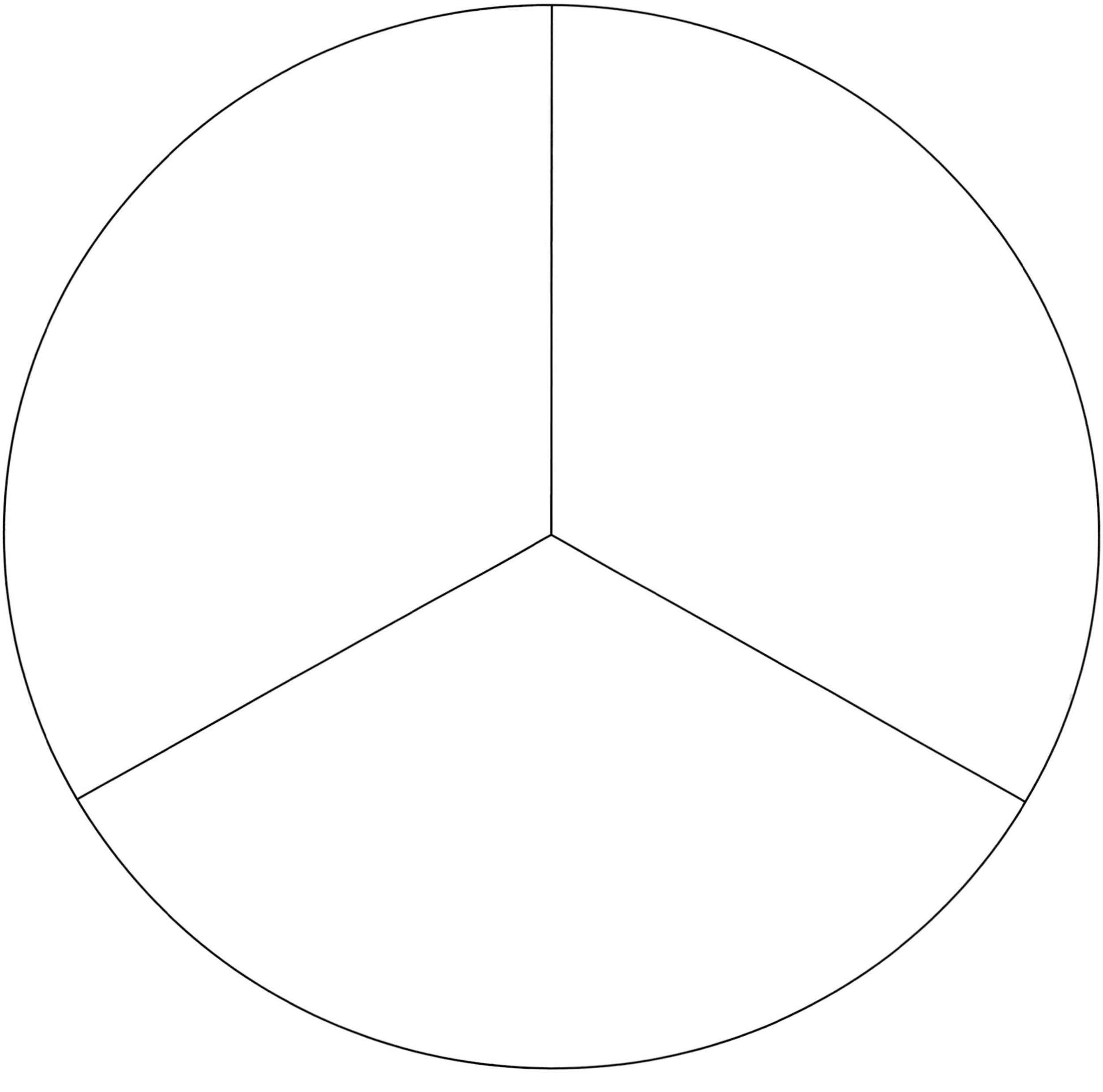

Name: ______________________________

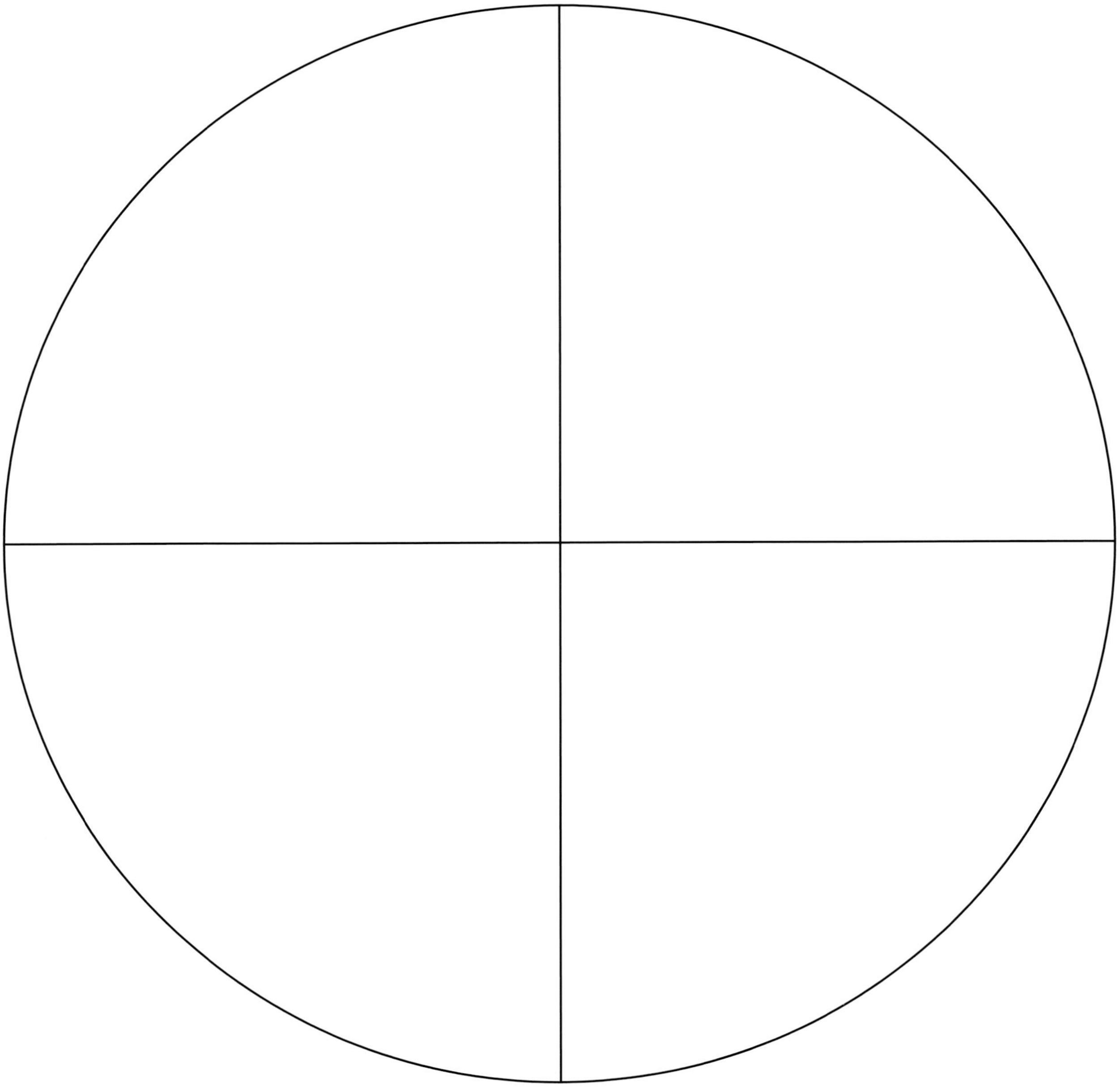

Name: ______________________________

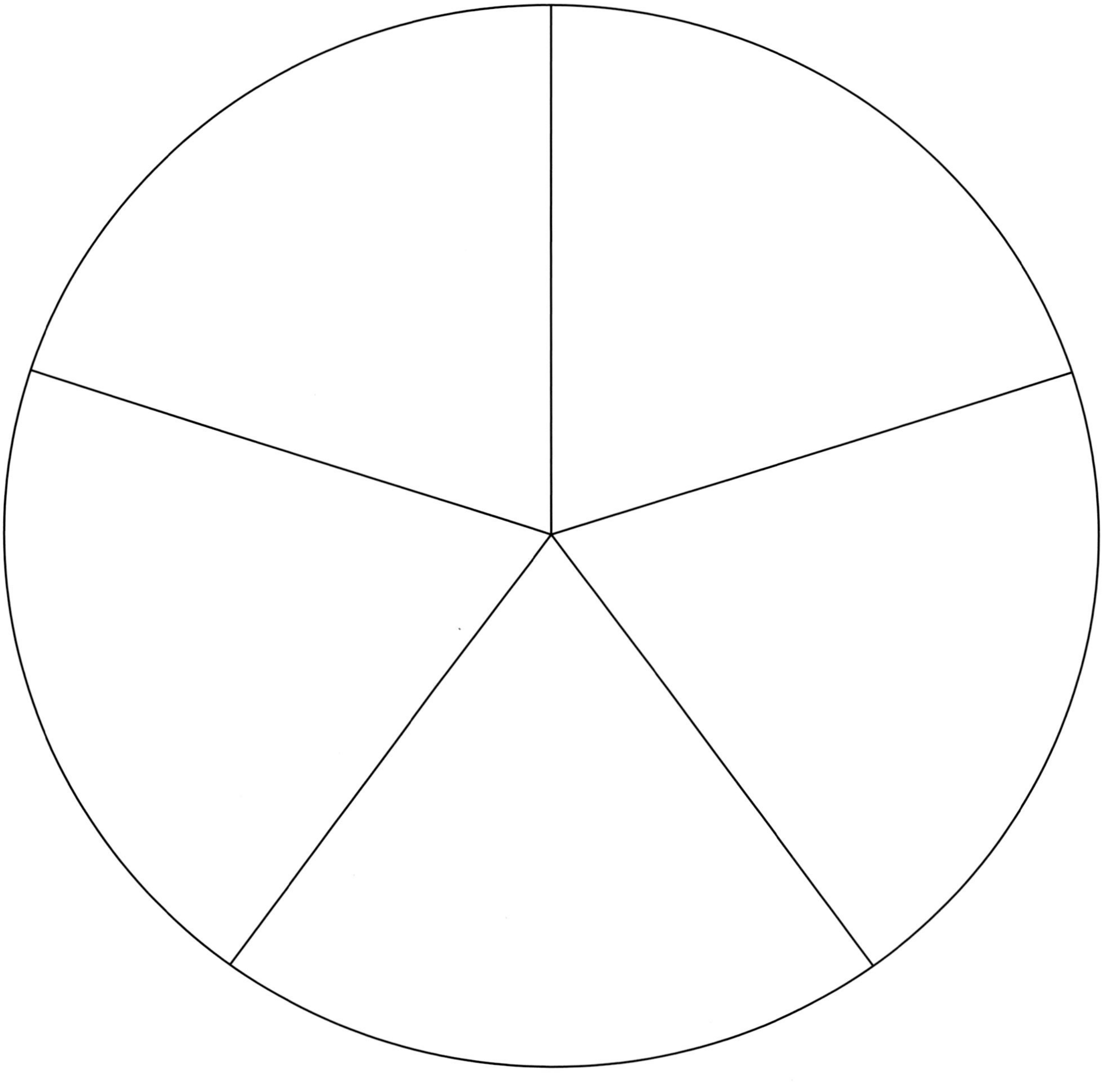

Name: ____________________

Name: ______________________________

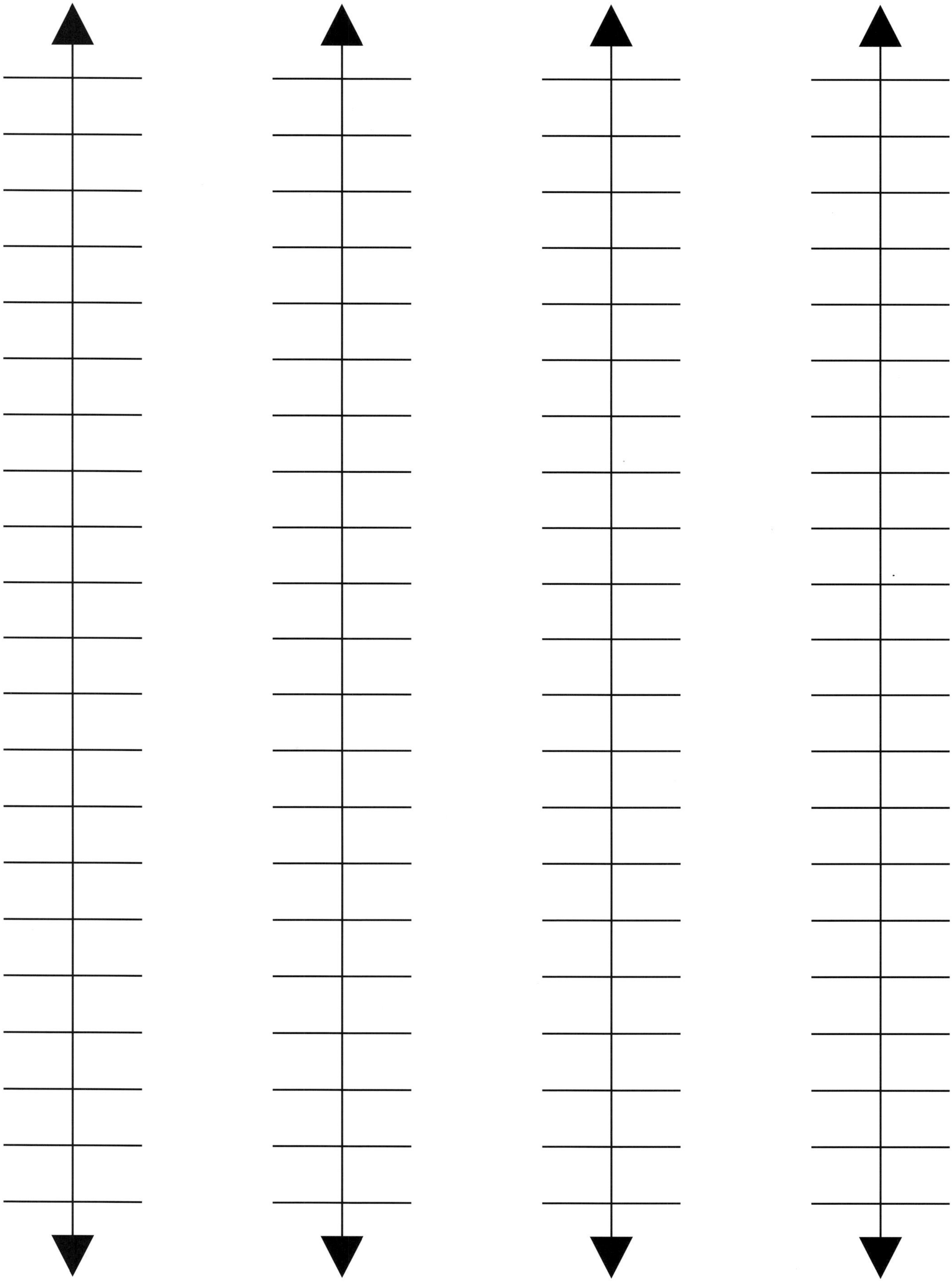

Name: ______________________________

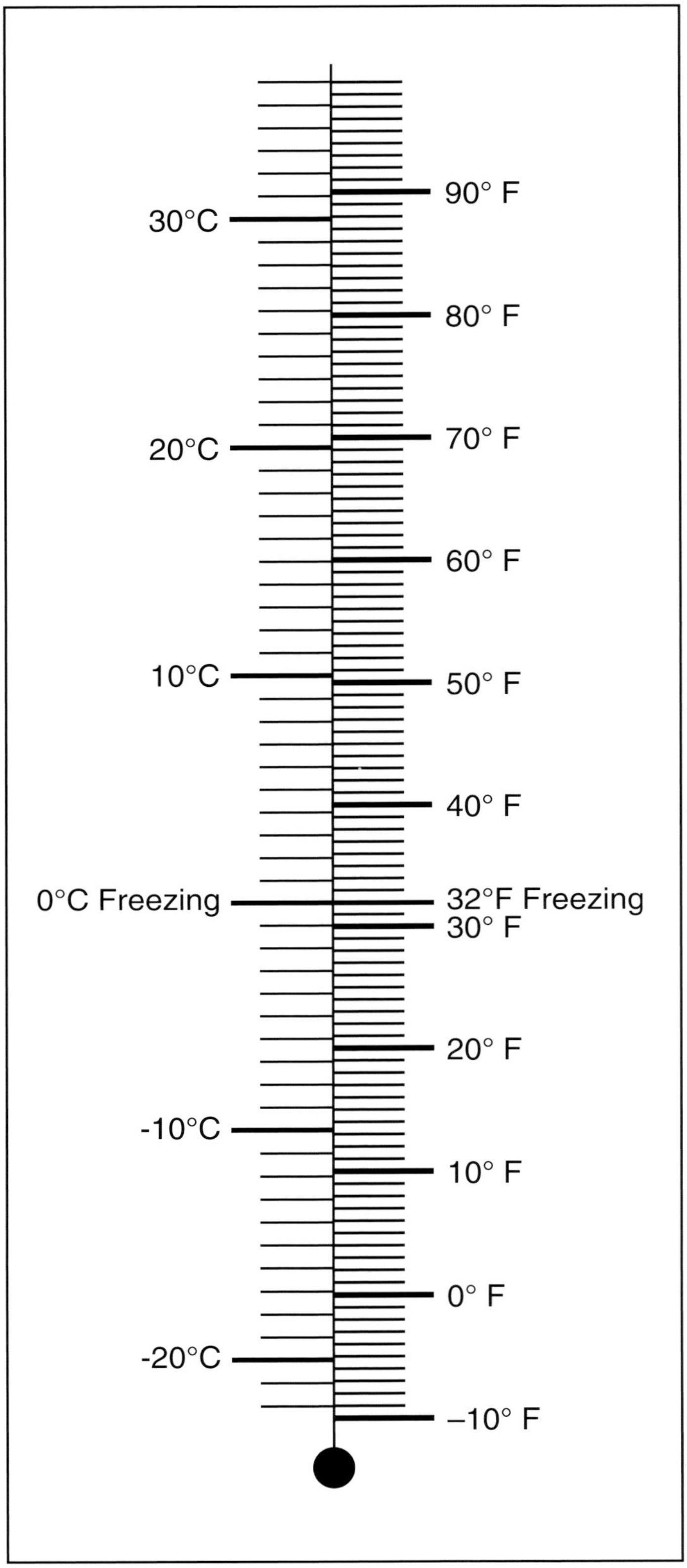

90° F
30°C
80° F
70° F
20°C
60° F
10°C
50° F
40° F
0°C Freezing
32°F Freezing
30° F
20° F
-10°C
10° F
0° F
-20°C
–10° F

Name: ______________________________

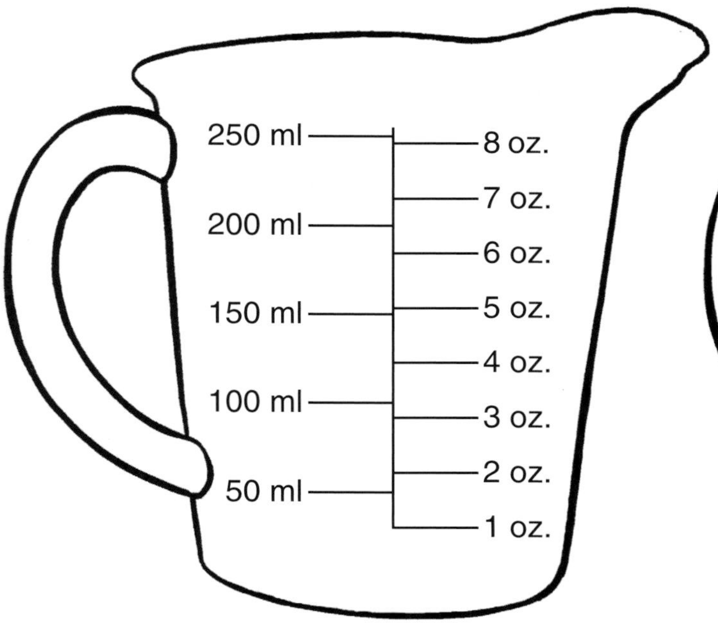
250 ml
200 ml
150 ml
100 ml
50 ml
8 oz.
7 oz.
6 oz.
5 oz.
4 oz.
3 oz.
2 oz.
1 oz.

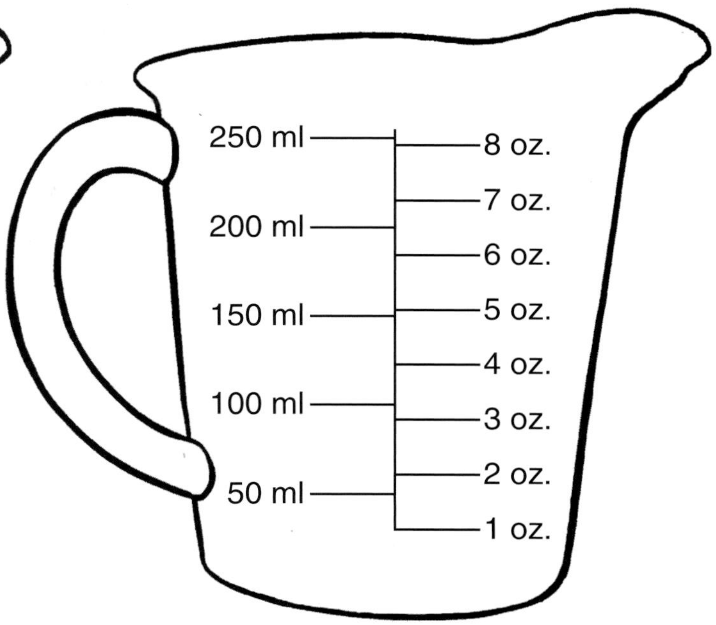
250 ml
200 ml
150 ml
100 ml
50 ml
8 oz.
7 oz.
6 oz.
5 oz.
4 oz.
3 oz.
2 oz.
1 oz.

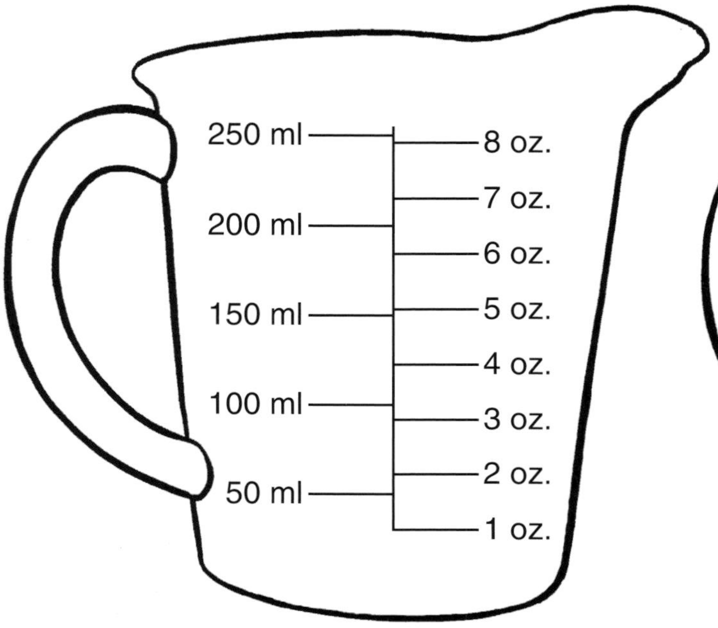
250 ml
200 ml
150 ml
100 ml
50 ml
8 oz.
7 oz.
6 oz.
5 oz.
4 oz.
3 oz.
2 oz.
1 oz.

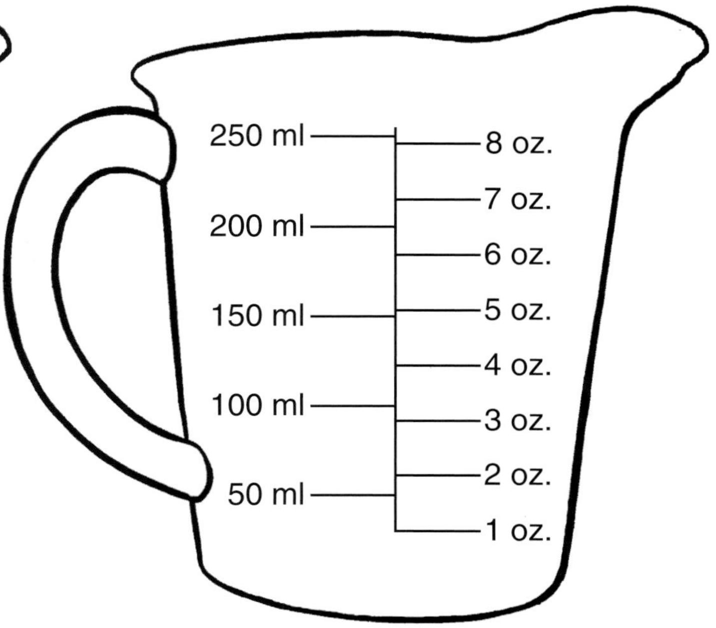
250 ml
200 ml
150 ml
100 ml
50 ml
8 oz.
7 oz.
6 oz.
5 oz.
4 oz.
3 oz.
2 oz.
1 oz.

Name: ________________________________

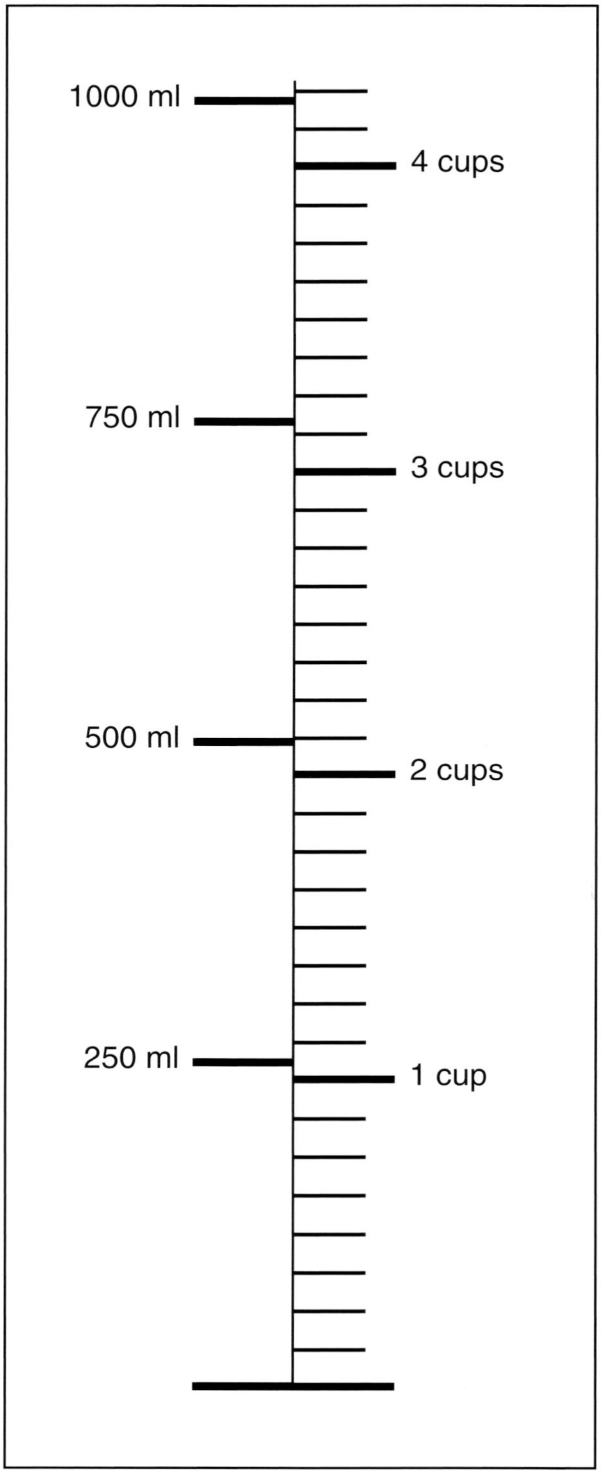

Name: ______________________________

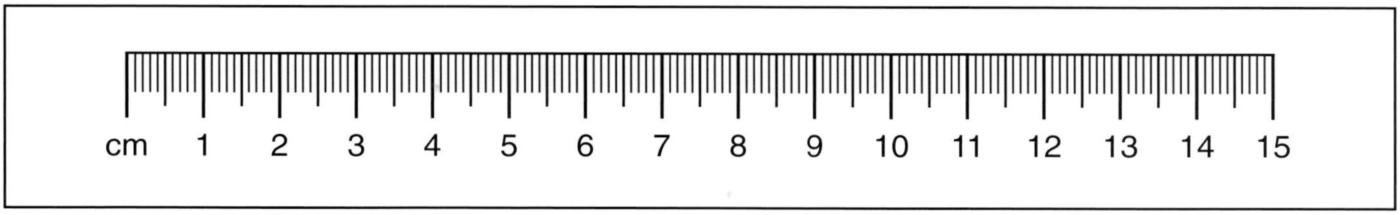
cm 1 2 3 4 5 6 7 8 9 10 11 12 13 14 15

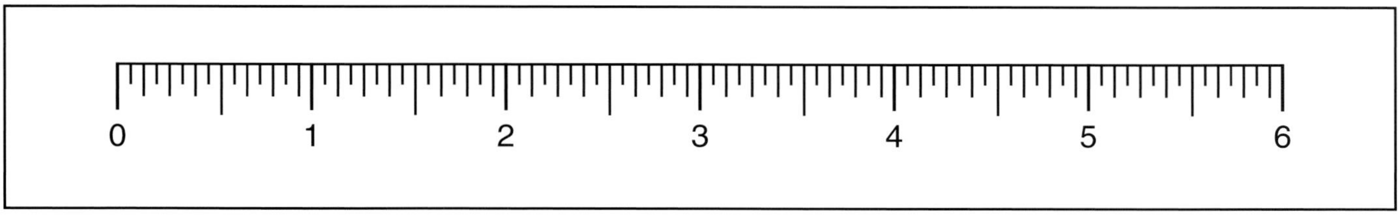
0 1 2 3 4 5 6

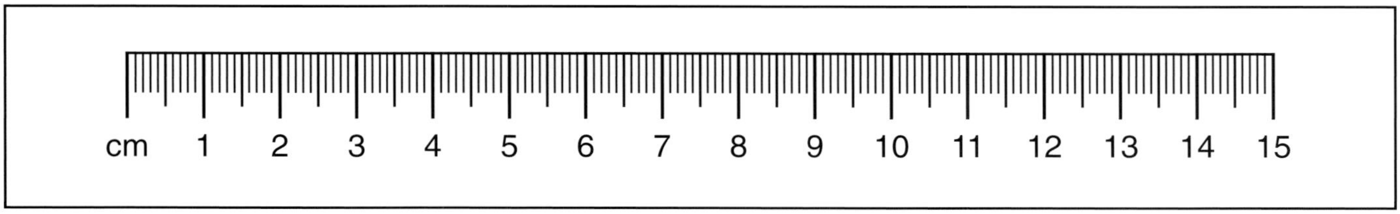
cm 1 2 3 4 5 6 7 8 9 10 11 12 13 14 15

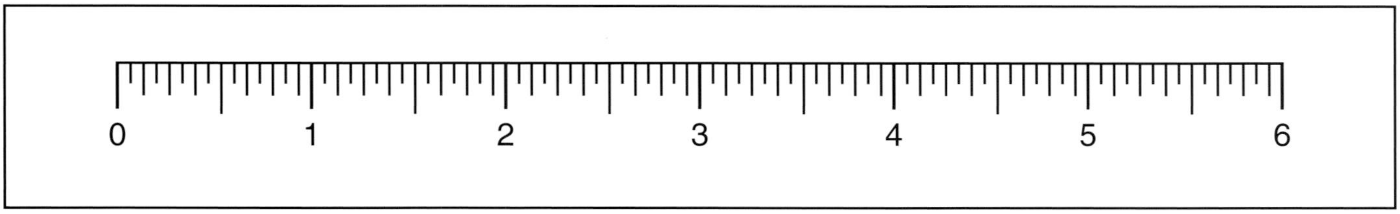
0 1 2 3 4 5 6

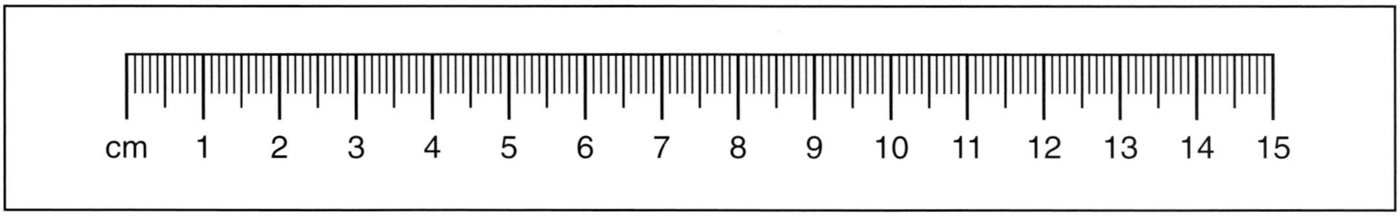
cm 1 2 3 4 5 6 7 8 9 10 11 12 13 14 15

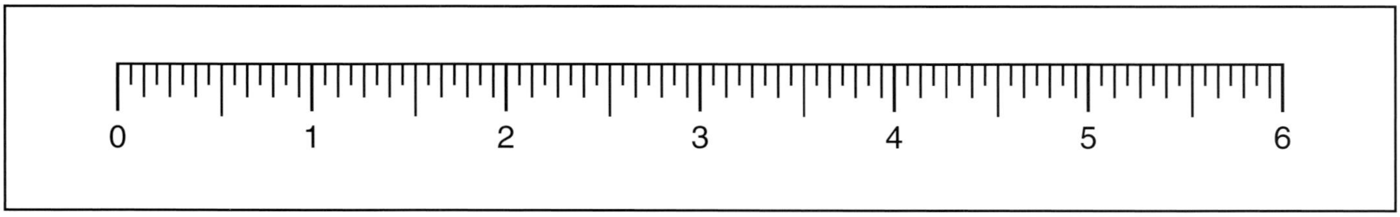
0 1 2 3 4 5 6

Name: ____________________

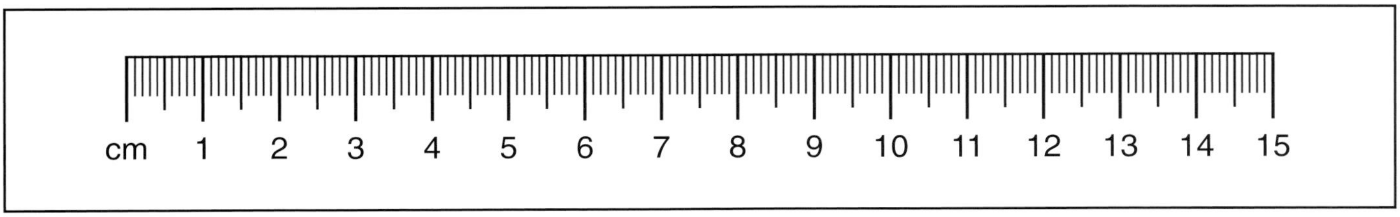
cm 1 2 3 4 5 6 7 8 9 10 11 12 13 14 15

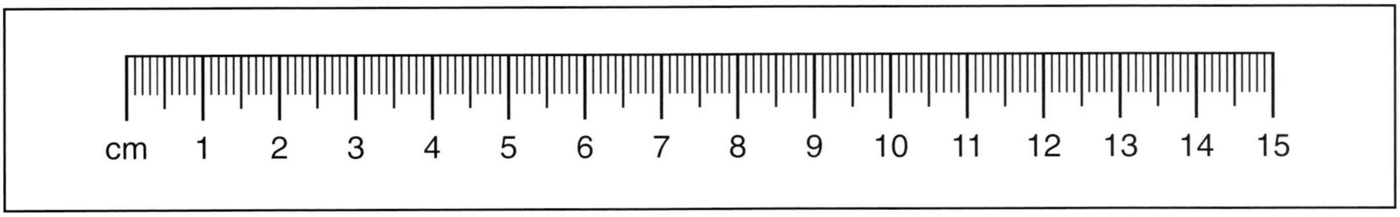
cm 1 2 3 4 5 6 7 8 9 10 11 12 13 14 15

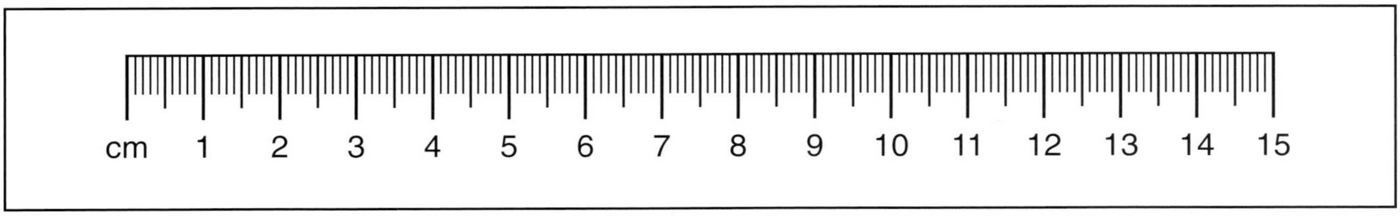
cm 1 2 3 4 5 6 7 8 9 10 11 12 13 14 15

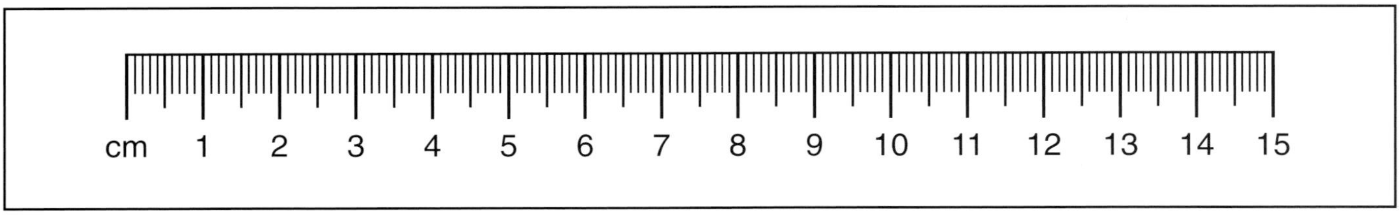
cm 1 2 3 4 5 6 7 8 9 10 11 12 13 14 15

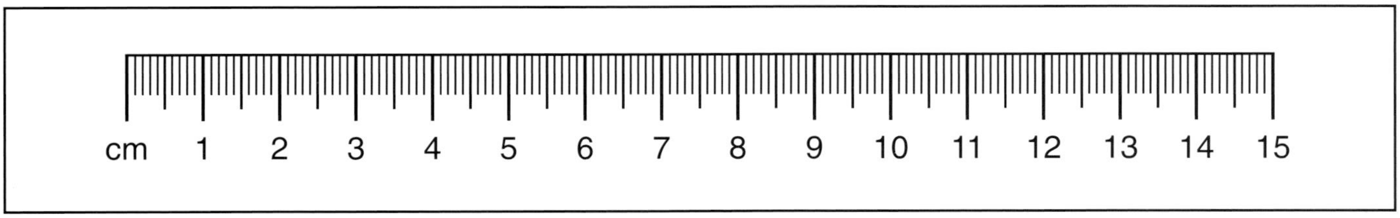
cm 1 2 3 4 5 6 7 8 9 10 11 12 13 14 15

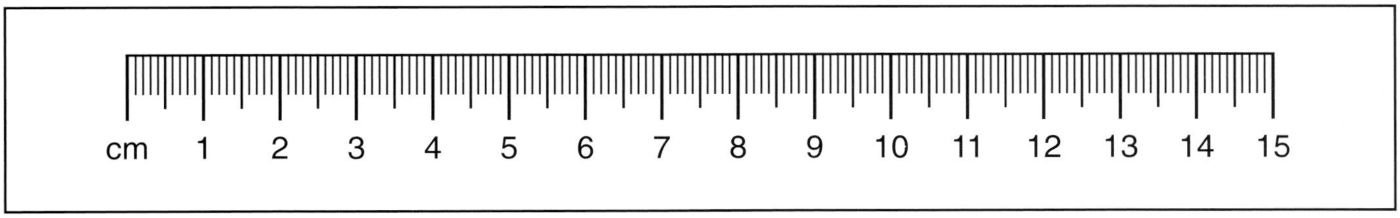
cm 1 2 3 4 5 6 7 8 9 10 11 12 13 14 15

Name: ____________________

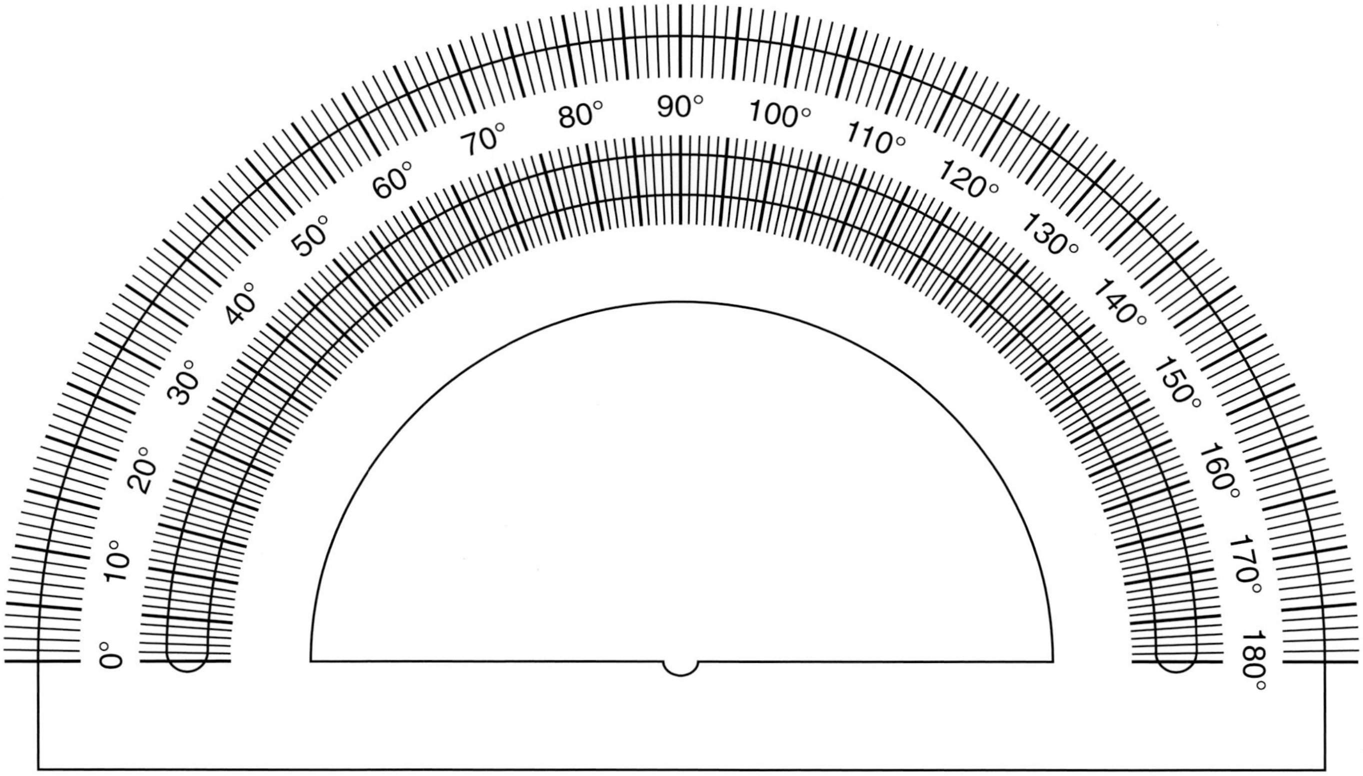

Name: ____________________

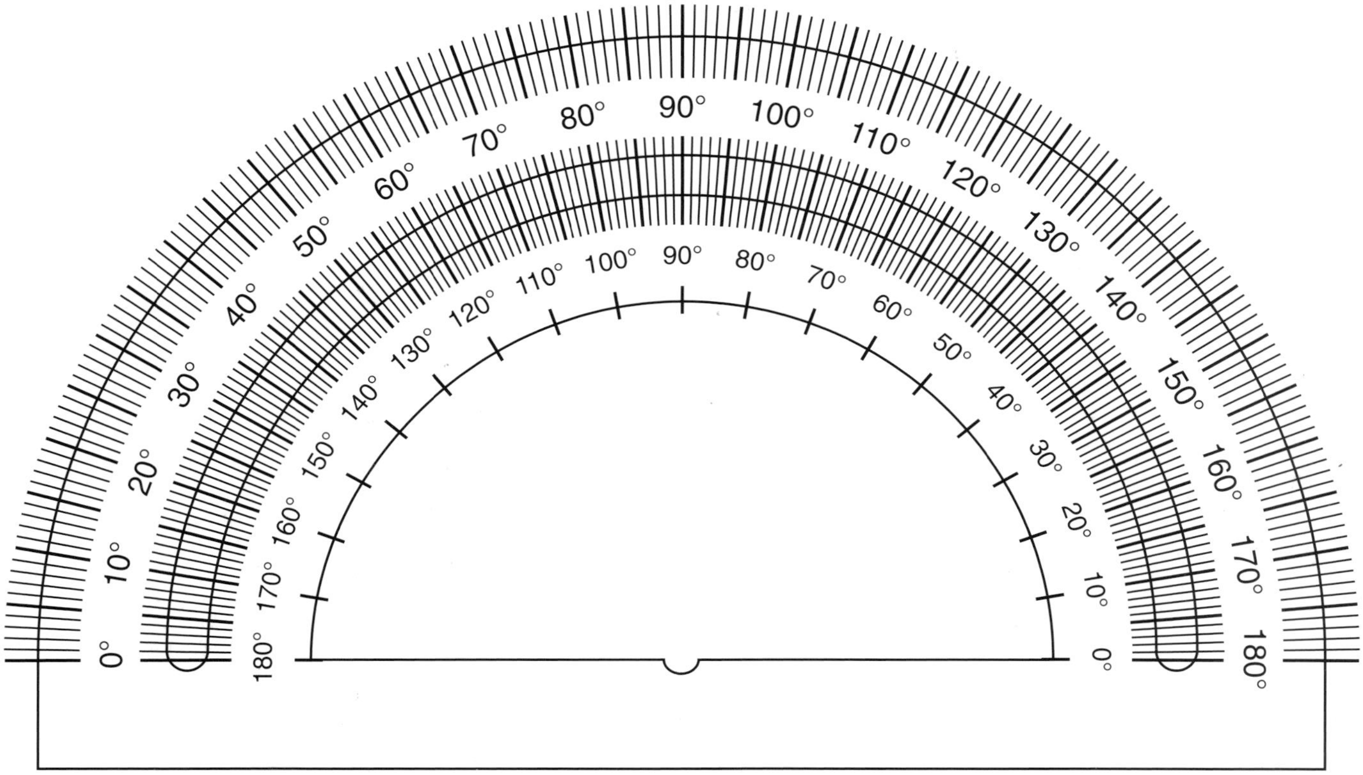
0° 10° 20° 30° 40° 50° 60° 70° 80° 90° 100° 110° 120° 130° 140° 150° 160° 170° 180°
180° 170° 160° 150° 140° 130° 120° 110° 100° 90° 80° 70° 60° 50° 40° 30° 20° 10° 0°